M337 Unit D1
Mathematics: A Third Level Course

COMPLEX ANALYSIS

UNIT D1 CONFORMAL MAPPINGS

Prepared by the Course Team

Before working through this text, make sure that you have read the
Course Guide for M337 Complex Analysis.

The Open University, Walton Hall, Milton Keynes, MK7 6AA.

First published 1993. Reprinted 1995, 1999, 2003, 2006

Edited, designed and typeset by the Open University using the Open University T$_E$X System.

Printed in Malta by Gutenberg Press Limited.

ISBN 0 7492 2186 0

This text forms part of an Open University Third Level Course. If you would like a copy of
Studying with The Open University, please write to the Central Enquiry Service,
PO Box 200, The Open University, Walton Hall, Milton Keynes, MK7 6YZ. If you have not
already enrolled on the Course and would like to buy this or other Open University material,
please write to Open University Educational Enterprises Ltd, 12 Cofferidge Close, Stony
Stratford, Milton Keynes, MK11 1BY, United Kingdom.

1.4

CONTENTS

INTRODUCTION

In this unit we continue the discussion of conformal functions that we began in *Unit A4*. There we described a function as *conformal* if it preserves angles between smooth paths. We also proved that any analytic function is conformal on a region, provided that its derivative is never zero there.

Unit A4, Theorem 4.2

Much of the present unit is concerned with developing techniques for finding the images of regions under various conformal functions, or *conformal mappings* as they are often called. We shall also look at techniques for finding specific one-one conformal mappings which map one given region onto another. Such techniques will prove useful in *Unit D2* when we study fluid flow around an obstacle.

Not all conformal mappings are one-one; for example, the function $f(z) = e^z$ is conformal but it is not one-one.

Many of the regions we consider have boundaries that consist of arcs of circles and line segments. By understanding how lines and circles behave under various conformal mappings, we can sometimes see how to map the boundary of one such region onto another. Having dealt with the boundary, we can then deal with the region it encloses.

In Section 1, we show that linear functions and the reciprocal function 'preserve' lines and circles, that is, they map any line or circle to a line or a circle. We also introduce the *point at infinity* and the *extended complex plane*, which make it possible to think of a line extended to infinity as a *generalized circle*.

In Section 2, we consider the class of all functions that can be obtained by composing linear functions and the reciprocal function. These functions are called *Möbius transformations*. We analyse the properties of these transformations and show that any line or circle can be mapped to any other line or circle by a suitable Möbius transformation.

In Section 3, we develop techniques for finding the images of lines and circles under a Möbius transformation. One of these techniques leads to a different type of equation for a circle, known as the *Apollonian form*. To help us analyse this form, we introduce the notion of *inverse points* with respect to a circle.

In Section 4, we use the techniques from Section 3 to find Möbius transformations that map one disc or half-plane onto another. We then explore ways of constructing conformal mappings between more general regions by composing Möbius transformations with some of the other conformal mappings that have been introduced in the course.

Finally, in Section 5, we discuss a remarkable theorem due to Riemann which states that under certain circumstances we can always find a one-one conformal mapping from a simply-connected region (other than $\mathbb{C}$) onto the unit disc.

Remark Note that all the one-one conformal mappings which we discuss are in fact given by one-one analytic functions and so the name 'conformal mapping' may seem unnecessary. However, it is traditional to use this name when discussing such mappings from a geometric point of view.

Study guide

The material in the first three sections paves the way for the work on regions in Section 4, which is the most important section of the unit. In particular, the audio tape in Subsection 4.3 contains material on the inverse trigonometric functions that we promised earlier in the course. Also Subsection 4.4 contains material on the so-called *Joukowski function* that will be needed in *Unit D2*. Section 5 is intended for reading only.

1 LINEAR AND RECIPROCAL FUNCTIONS

After working through this section, you should be able to:

(a) write down a linear function which maps one given region onto another of the same shape;

(b) find the image of a circle or line under the reciprocal function;

(c) determine the extended function associated with a suitable analytic function;

(d) visualize the extended complex plane as the Riemann sphere.

1.1 Linear functions

Perhaps the simplest conformal mappings are those that map regions of the complex plane onto one another without distortion. For example, consider the function $f(z) = (1 + i)z$. In *Unit A2*, Section 3, we investigated the behaviour of f by examining its effect on a Cartesian grid. We showed that f scales the grid by the factor $|1 + i| = \sqrt{2}$ and rotates it about the origin through the angle $\text{Arg}(1 + i) = \pi/4$, as shown in Figure 1.1.

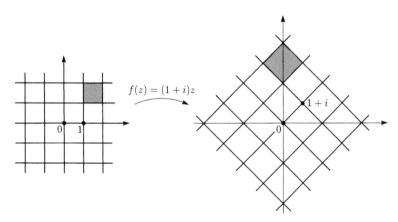

Figure 1.1

Straight lines map to straight lines, angles are preserved (because the function is conformal) and so the shaded square region remains square.

Scalings and rotations are not the only transformations of the complex plane that leave shapes of regions unaltered. Translations and reflections also preserve shapes. In this unit we are not interested in reflections because they reverse the orientation of angles and hence fail to be conformal. Translations, on the other hand, are functions of the form $f(z) = z + b$ (see Figure 1.2) and these are certainly conformal mappings.

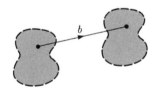

Figure 1.2

In general, any conformal mapping that preserves shapes can be expressed as a composition of a scaling, followed by a rotation, followed by a translation; it can therefore be written in the form $f(z) = az + b$, where $a \neq 0$. Functions of this form are called *linear functions*, because they map straight lines onto straight lines.

Definition A function of the form $f(z) = az + b$, where $a, b \in \mathbb{C}$ and $a \neq 0$, is called a **linear function**.

Note that the coefficients a and b are complex numbers.

Given any two regions $\mathcal{R}$ and $\mathcal{S}$ in the complex plane which have the same shape (see Figure 1.3), it is easy to see how to construct a linear function that sends $\mathcal{R}$ onto $\mathcal{S}$. We first scale $\mathcal{R}$ by a positive factor r to obtain a region of the same size as $\mathcal{S}$. Next we rotate through an angle θ about the origin, to obtain a region that is aligned with $\mathcal{S}$. Finally we superimpose the region on $\mathcal{S}$ by a translation by c units parallel to the real axis and d units parallel to the imaginary axis. The required function is then $f(z) = \left(re^{i\theta}\right)z + (c + id)$, which is clearly a linear function.

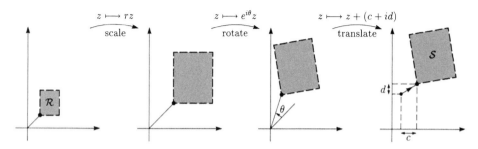

Figure 1.3

Example 1.1

Find a linear function that maps the region $\mathbb{C} - \{x \in \mathbb{R} : x \leq 0\}$ onto the region $\mathbb{C} - \{iy : y \geq 2\}$.

Solution

Figure 1.4 shows that both regions have the same (unbounded) shape.

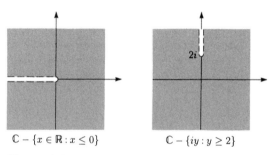

$$\mathbb{C} - \{x \in \mathbb{R} : x \leq 0\} \qquad \mathbb{C} - \{iy : y \geq 2\}$$

Figure 1.4

Clearly we can map the first region onto the second region by a rotation through $-\pi/2$ followed by a translation of 2 units in the direction of the positive imaginary axis. No scaling is necessary. A suitable linear function is therefore

$$f(z) = e^{-i\pi/2}z + 2i = -iz + 2i. \qquad \blacksquare$$

Notice that a linear function from one region onto another is not necessarily unique. Indeed, in Example 1.1 we could have scaled the region on the left by any positive factor, r say, before carrying out the rotation and the translation, to give the linear function $f(z) = -irz + 2i$.

Problem 1.1 _____

Sketch the discs $D_1 = \{z : |z| < 2\}$ and $D_2 = \{z : |z - (1 + i)| < 4\}$ and find a linear function that maps D_1 onto D_2.

_____

As we mentioned in the Introduction, one of the main aims of this unit is to find conformal mappings that map one region onto another. In Problem 1.1, you were asked to find a linear function that sends D_1 onto D_2. Notice, however, that the boundary of D_1 is mapped to the boundary of D_2 along with the discs, and so you could have found the function by concentrating on the circular boundaries of D_1 and D_2.

For linear functions this observation about boundaries is hardly worth making, but for other conformal mappings it is often easier to consider what happens to the boundary of a region before you deal with the region itself. For this reason, we shall spend the rest of this section and most of Sections 2 and 3 discussing circles and lines, subsets of which typically form the boundaries of the regions that we wish to consider. We shall return to the regions themselves in Section 4.

We begin by noting that the technique illustrated in Figure 1.3 gives the following result when applied to pairs of circles and pairs of lines.

Theorem 1.1 Linear functions map circles onto circles and straight lines onto straight lines. Furthermore,

(a) given any two circles C_1 and C_2, there is a linear function that maps C_1 onto C_2;

(b) given any two lines L_1 and L_2, there is a linear function that maps L_1 onto L_2.

Now suppose that we wish to find a conformal mapping that maps a straight line onto a circle. The function cannot be linear, since a circle is not the same shape as a line, so what sort of function can we use? We turn our attention to this next.

1.2 The reciprocal function

The **reciprocal function** is defined by $f(z) = 1/z$; its domain and image are $\mathbb{C} - \{0\}$. In *Unit A2*, Section 3, we investigated the behaviour of this function by examining its effect on Cartesian and polar grids. The effect that f has on a Cartesian grid is shown in Figure 1.5.

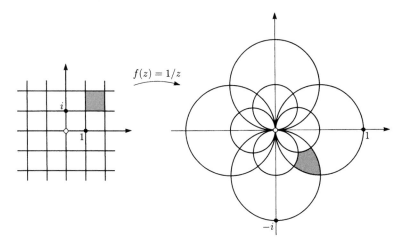

Figure 1.5

This suggests that the reciprocal function might be the kind of function that we need in order to map lines onto circles. Indeed, apart from the lines that pass through the origin, each grid line is mapped to a circle. The next example shows what happens to a line which is not parallel to an axis.

Example 1.2

Find the equation for the image of the line $3y - 4x = 2$ under the reciprocal function $f(z) = 1/z$.

Solution

Let $w = u + iv$ be the image of an arbitrary point $z = x + iy$ on the line $3y - 4x = 2$. Since $w = f(z) = 1/z$, it follows that $z = 1/w$ and hence that

$$x + iy = \frac{1}{u + iv} = \frac{u - iv}{u^2 + v^2}.$$

Equating real parts and imaginary parts, we find that

$$x = \frac{u}{u^2 + v^2}, \quad y = \frac{-v}{u^2 + v^2}.$$

Since x and y satisfy the equation $3y - 4x = 2$, it follows that u and v must satisfy the equation

$$3\left(\frac{-v}{u^2 + v^2}\right) - 4\left(\frac{u}{u^2 + v^2}\right) = 2.$$

If we multiply both sides of the above equation by $u^2 + v^2$, then we obtain the simpler equation,

$$-3v - 4u = 2\left(u^2 + v^2\right).$$

Rearranging the terms and completing the squares, we obtain

$$(u + 1)^2 + \left(v + \tfrac{3}{4}\right)^2 = \tfrac{25}{16}.$$

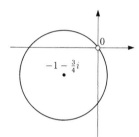

Figure 1.6

This is the equation of the circle with radius $\frac{5}{4}$ and centre $-1 - \frac{3}{4}i$. We shall see later that the image is the whole of this circle except for 0 (see Figure 1.6). ■

There is nothing special about the line $3y - 4x = 2$ in the above example. We can use the same method to find the equation for the image of various other paths. We summarize the method in the form of a strategy.

Strategy for finding the equation of the image of a path under $f(z) = 1/z$

To find the equation of the image $f(\Gamma)$ of a path Γ under $f(z) = 1/z$:

(a) write down an equation that relates the x- and y-coordinates of all points $x + iy$ on Γ;

(b) replace x by $\dfrac{u}{u^2 + v^2}$ and y by $\dfrac{-v}{u^2 + v^2}$;

(c) simplify the resulting equation to obtain an equation that relates the u- and v-coordinates of all points $u + iv$ on the image $f(\Gamma)$.

This is different from the strategy used in *Unit A2*, Subsection 2.2, and it applies only to the reciprocal function.

As we mentioned in Example 1.2, the strategy may yield an equation that is satisfied by some points that do not lie on the image (for example, the origin in Figure 1.6). We show how to deal with such missing points later in this section.

Problem 1.2

Use the above strategy to find the equation for the image of the line $y + 4x = 1$ under the reciprocal function.

If a line (or circle) passes through the origin, which does not lie in the domain of the reciprocal function, then we must be content to find an equation for the image of what remains of the line (or circle) after the origin has been removed.

We indicate one way to deal with the origin later in this section.

Problem 1.3

Find the equation for the image of the line $y - x = 0$ (with the origin removed) under the reciprocal function.

So far we have used the strategy to find equations for the images of straight lines under the reciprocal function. Some lines map to lines, whereas others map to circles. We now turn our attention to the images of circles.

Example 1.3

Find the equation for the image of the circle $(x-1)^2 + (y-2)^2 = 9$ under the reciprocal function.

Solution

The equation of the circle can be rewritten as

$$x^2 + y^2 - 2x - 4y - 4 = 0.$$

This circle does not pass through the origin.

On replacing x by $u/(u^2+v^2)$ and y by $-v/(u^2+v^2)$, we obtain

$$\left(\frac{u}{u^2+v^2}\right)^2 + \left(\frac{-v}{u^2+v^2}\right)^2 - 2\left(\frac{u}{u^2+v^2}\right) - 4\left(\frac{-v}{u^2+v^2}\right) - 4 = 0.$$

Here, the first two terms combine to give $\dfrac{u^2+(-v)^2}{(u^2+v^2)^2} = \dfrac{1}{u^2+v^2}$ and so the equation becomes

$$\left(\frac{1}{u^2+v^2}\right) - 2\left(\frac{u}{u^2+v^2}\right) - 4\left(\frac{-v}{u^2+v^2}\right) - 4 = 0.$$

On multiplying this equation by u^2+v^2, we obtain

$$1 - 2u + 4v - 4(u^2+v^2) = 0,$$

that is,

$$(u^2+v^2) + \tfrac{1}{2}u - v - \tfrac{1}{4} = 0.$$

By completing the squares, we obtain

$$\left(u + \tfrac{1}{4}\right)^2 + \left(v - \tfrac{1}{2}\right)^2 = \tfrac{9}{16},$$

which is a circle of radius $\tfrac{3}{4}$ centred at $-\tfrac{1}{4} + \tfrac{1}{2}i$. ■

Problem 1.4

Find the equation for the image of each of the following circles under the reciprocal function.

(a) $x^2 + y^2 = 4$ (b) $(x-3)^2 + (y-4)^2 = 25$

In part (b) the origin must be removed.

It appears from the above examples and problems that the reciprocal function maps any circle or line to a circle or line, with 0 omitted if necessary. To prove this in general, we need the following result.

Theorem 1.2 Every line or circle has an equation of the form

$$a(x^2+y^2) + bx + cy + d = 0, \text{ where } a,b,c,d \in \mathbb{R} \text{ and } b^2 + c^2 > 4ad. \quad (1.1)$$

Conversely, any such equation represents a line or a circle.

Also

(a) the equation represents a line if and only if $a = 0$;

(b) the line or circle passes through the origin if and only if $d = 0$.

Proof If $a = 0$, then Equation (1.1) represents a line, because the condition $b^2 + c^2 > 0$ holds if and only if b and c are not both zero.

If $a \neq 0$, then we can divide through by a and complete the squares, to obtain the following equation, which is equivalent to Equation (1.1):

$$\left(x + \frac{b}{2a}\right)^2 + \left(y + \frac{c}{2a}\right)^2 = \frac{b^2 + c^2 - 4ad}{4a^2}.$$

This last equation represents a circle if and only if $b^2 + c^2 > 4ad$.

Finally, the line or circle passes through the origin if and only if $x = y = 0$ is a solution of Equation (1.1), and this happens if and only if $d = 0$. ∎

It is now easy to use an argument similar to that used in Example 1.3 to find the image of a general line or circle under the reciprocal transformation.

Problem 1.5

(a) Show that the non-zero points on the line or circle

$$a\left(x^2 + y^2\right) + bx + cy + d = 0, \quad \text{where } a, b, c, d \in \mathbb{R} \text{ and } b^2 + c^2 > 4ad,$$

are mapped under the reciprocal function to points on the line or circle

$$d\left(u^2 + v^2\right) + bu - cv + a = 0, \quad \text{where } a, b, c, d \in \mathbb{R} \text{ and } b^2 + (-c)^2 > 4da,$$

and vice versa.

(b) Deduce that the reciprocal function maps:

(i)	a line through the origin	to	a line through the origin;
(ii)	a line not through the origin	to	a circle through the origin;
(iii)	a circle through the origin	to	a line not through the origin;
(iv)	a circle not through the origin	to	a circle not through the origin.

In each case, the origin is *not* included in the circle or line through the origin.

Note that (iii) is the converse of (ii) and reflects the fact that the reciprocal function is its own inverse.

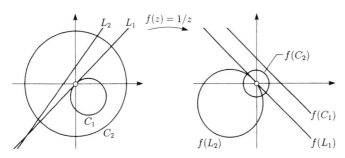

Figure 1.7

There is no need to remember the results in part (b) of Problem 1.5, which are illustrated in Figure 1.7, since they can be recalled intuitively as follows. First of all, points on a line or circle that passes through the origin can be chosen arbitrarily close to the origin. The images of such points will then be arbitrarily far from the origin and must therefore lie on a line. Secondly, points on a line can be chosen arbitrarily far from the origin. The images of these points will then be arbitrarily close to the origin and must therefore lie on a circle or line through the origin. With a little practice, it is easy to use these two observations to predict the form taken by the image of any line or circle under the reciprocal function.

Problem 1.6 _____

For each of the following lines and circles, decide whether its image under the reciprocal function is a line or a circle, and whether it passes through the origin.

(a) $2x + 3y = 6$ (b) $x^2 + (y-1)^2 = 1$

(c) $x^2 + (y-1)^2 = 2$ (d) $2x - 3y = 0$

1.3 The point at infinity

The above discussion about the reciprocal function was rather untidy because of the differing properties of lines and circles, and because of the various exceptional cases involving the origin. We can deal with both difficulties in a rather elegant way by adding an additional point to the complex plane.

To see how this works, consider the correspondence between the circle and line that you investigated in Problem 1.4(b) (see Figure 1.8).

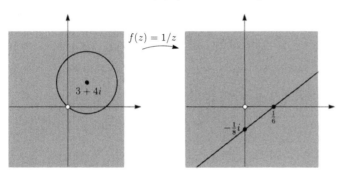

Figure 1.8

Here the 'gap' in the circle in the z-plane arises because the origin is not contained in the domain of the function $f(z) = 1/z$. In *Unit B4*, Section 1, you saw that if a function f has a removable singularity at a point α, then we can 'fill the gap' at α by defining

$$f(\alpha) = \lim_{z \to \alpha} f(z).$$

The trouble with using this approach to 'fill the gap' in the domain of the reciprocal function at 0, is that $f(z) = 1/z$ has a pole at 0 and so $f(z) \to \infty$ as $z \to 0$. It is therefore meaningless to define

$$f(0) = \lim_{z \to 0} f(z),$$

since the limit does not exist. One way to overcome this limitation is to attach an additional *point at infinity* to the complex plane.

Definition   The **extended complex plane** $\widehat{\mathbb{C}}$ is the union of the ordinary complex plane $\mathbb{C}$ and one extra point, the **point at infinity**, which is denoted by ∞; thus $\widehat{\mathbb{C}} = \mathbb{C} \cup \{\infty\}$.

$\widehat{\mathbb{C}}$ is read 'C-hat'.

If a function f has a pole at α, then, provided that we are prepared to work in $\widehat{\mathbb{C}}$, we can extend the definition of f to α by defining $f(\alpha) = \infty$. For example, we can extend the definition of the reciprocal function $f(z) = 1/z$ to 0, by defining $f(0) = \infty$.

Having introduced the point at infinity, it is natural to ask whether we can extend the definition of the reciprocal function to the whole of $\widehat{\mathbb{C}}$, by defining its value at ∞. It turns out that we can, and we do it by defining the behaviour of a function f at ∞ in terms of the behaviour of the related function $g(w) = f(1/w)$ near 0.

> **Definitions** A function f has a **removable singularity**, a **pole of order k**, or an **essential singularity at ∞**, if the function $g(w) = f(1/w)$ has the corresponding type of singularity at 0.

The substitution $w = 1/z$ takes a point z near ∞ to a point w near 0.

If a function f has a removable singularity at ∞, then we can remove the singularity by defining

$$f(\infty) = \lim_{w \to 0} f(1/w).$$

Also, if f has a pole at ∞, then we can remove it by defining $f(\infty) = \infty$.

Note that if $f(\infty) = \lambda$, where $\lambda \in \mathbb{C}$ or $\lambda = \infty$, then we say that '$f(z)$ tends to λ as z tends to infinity' and we write $f(z) \to \lambda$ as $z \to \infty$.

Any rational function f is defined throughout $\widehat{\mathbb{C}}$ except at its poles and removable singularities. By removing these singularities in the way described above, we obtain a function with domain $\widehat{\mathbb{C}}$, known as the **extended function** associated with f. We shall use the notation $\widehat{f}$ for this extended function to emphasize that its domain is $\widehat{\mathbb{C}}$.

The only functions that can be extended to $\widehat{\mathbb{C}}$ in this way are rational functions.

Many texts do not distinguish between the functions f and $\widehat{f}$.

Note that all the results from the course about analytic functions apply only to f. If necessary, however, we could extend concepts such as continuity and differentiability to apply to $\widehat{f}$ at ∞, by using the $g(w) = f(1/w)$ approach.

See *Unit D3*, Section 1.

Example 1.4

Determine the extended function $\widehat{f}$ associated with the function

$$f(z) = \frac{4z + 5}{2z - 3}.$$

Solution

Since

$$f(z) \to \infty \text{ as } z \to \tfrac{3}{2},$$

it follows that f has a pole at $\frac{3}{2}$, and so $\widehat{f}\left(\frac{3}{2}\right) = \infty$. Also

$$\lim_{w \to 0} f(1/w) = \lim_{w \to 0} \frac{(4/w) + 5}{(2/w) - 3} = \lim_{w \to 0} \frac{4 + 5w}{2 - 3w} = 2,$$

and so f has a removable singularity at ∞, with $\widehat{f}(\infty) = 2$. Hence

Note that we do *not* attempt to perform arithmetic operations with ∞.

$$\widehat{f}(z) = \begin{cases} f(z), & z \in \mathbb{C} - \left\{\frac{3}{2}\right\}, \\ \infty, & z = \frac{3}{2}, \\ 2, & z = \infty. \end{cases} \quad \blacksquare$$

Problem 1.7

Determine the extended function $\widehat{f}$ associated with each of the following functions f.

(a) $f(z) = \dfrac{6z + 4}{3z + 1}$ (b) $f(z) = \dfrac{1}{z}$ (c) $f(z) = 5z + 7$

(d) $f(z) = \dfrac{1}{2z + 1}$ (e) $f(z) = \dfrac{z^2 + 1}{z}$

Under the extended reciprocal function, the exceptional cases involving the origin and the distinction between lines and circles disappear. To see this, we look again at the correspondence between the circle and line that you investigated in Problem 1.4(b) (see Figure 1.8).

With the extended reciprocal function there is no longer a 'gap' in the circle, since the origin now maps to the point ∞. The trouble is that the image of the circle is no longer a line, but a line together with the point ∞, so we need to consider how such a set can be interpreted.

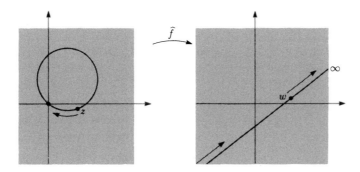

Figure 1.9

To do this, think of a point z on the circle in Figure 1.9 moving toward the origin from below. As it moves, its image $w = \widehat{f}(z) = 1/z$ moves up the line. The closer that z gets to the origin, the further w moves up the line. When z reaches the origin, its image $w = \widehat{f}(z)$ reaches ∞. After that, as z continues round the circle, w returns up the line from below. If you like, you can think of the point ∞ as linking together the two ends of the line, thereby enabling points to travel 'round and round' the line. By a stretch of the imagination, this allows us to think of the line as a circle of infinite radius which has a 'gap at infinity' that can be filled by the point ∞.

There is nothing special about the line in Figure 1.9. Indeed we can 'fill the gap' at infinity in any line L by forming the set $L \cup \{\infty\}$. Such a set is called an **extended line**. Since an extended line can be thought of as a circle of infinite radius, we make the following definition.

Definition A **generalized circle** is either a circle or an extended line.

Then we have the following result.

Theorem 1.3 Extended linear functions and the extended reciprocal function map

(a) $\widehat{\mathbb{C}}$ one-one onto $\widehat{\mathbb{C}}$;

(b) generalized circles onto generalized circles.

Proof First let $f(z) = az + b$ be any linear function. We already know that f maps $\mathbb{C}$ one-one onto $\mathbb{C}$, circles onto circles and lines onto lines. Since f has a pole at ∞, it follows that $\widehat{f}(\infty) = \infty$, and so $\widehat{f}$ maps $\widehat{\mathbb{C}}$ one-one onto $\widehat{\mathbb{C}}$ and extended lines onto extended lines.

Since $a \neq 0$, the function
$$g(w) = f(1/w) = a/w + b$$
has a pole at 0.

Next consider the reciprocal function $f(z) = 1/z$, which maps $\mathbb{C} - \{0\}$ one-one onto $\mathbb{C} - \{0\}$. If C_1 is a generalized circle, then we know that f maps $C_1 - \{0, \infty\}$ onto $C_2 - \{0, \infty\}$, where C_2 is another generalized circle. Since $\widehat{f}(0) = \infty$ and $\widehat{f}(\infty) = 0$, it follows that $\widehat{f}$ maps $\widehat{\mathbb{C}}$ one-one onto $\widehat{\mathbb{C}}$ and maps C_1 onto C_2. ∎

1.4 The Riemann sphere

Although the extended complex plane has helped us to explain the effect of the reciprocal function on generalized circles, there is something rather unsatisfactory about having to think of a straight line as a circle, since the 'ends' of the line appear to be infinitely far apart. It is also difficult to visualize where the point at infinity should be placed relative to $\mathbb{C}$, other than to think of it smeared in some vague way around the 'outer edge' of $\mathbb{C}$.

Fortunately there is a model of the extended complex plane in which the point at infinity actually appears as a genuine point. Imagine that the complex plane $\mathbb{C}$ is embedded in three-dimensional space, so that each complex number $x + iy$ is represented by the point $(x, y, 0)$ in the (x, y)-plane (see Figure 1.10). Now imagine a sphere $\mathbb{S}$ of unit radius, centred at the origin. This sphere is called the **Riemann sphere**. By analogy with the earth we shall refer to the point $N = (0, 0, 1)$ at the top of the sphere as the *North Pole*.

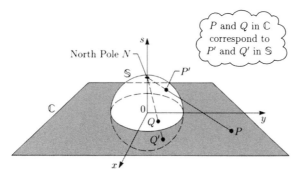

Figure 1.10

Each line that joins a point P in the complex plane to the North Pole intersects the Riemann sphere at a point P', say, and vice versa. In this way, we can associate all but one of the points P' on the Riemann sphere with the corresponding points P in the complex plane. The only point on the sphere that cannot be associated with a point in the complex plane is the North Pole. Of course P' can be moved arbitrarily close to the North Pole by choosing P sufficiently far from the origin, but P' never actually reaches the North Pole. To fill this gap, we associate the North Pole with the point ∞ in the extended complex plane $\widehat{\mathbb{C}}$.

The function $\pi : \mathbb{S} \longrightarrow \widehat{\mathbb{C}}$, which projects points on the Riemann sphere to the associated points in the extended complex plane, is called **stereographic projection**. Since this function is one-one and onto, we can use the Riemann sphere $\mathbb{S}$ as an alternative model of the extended complex plane $\widehat{\mathbb{C}}$.

One application to which the Riemann sphere is well suited is to help visualize generalized circles. To see this, consider a point P on a line L in $\mathbb{C}$ (see Figure 1.11).

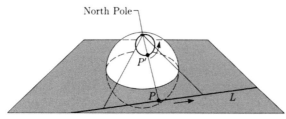

Figure 1.11

As P moves along L, the line that joins P to the North Pole sweeps out a plane that intersects the Riemann sphere in a circle. So as P moves along L, the corresponding point P' on the Riemann sphere traces out a circle. The further P moves out along the line, the closer P' gets to the North Pole. Notice, however, that P' never actually arrives at the North Pole. In fact, the North Pole corresponds to the gap in the line that we mentioned earlier. To fill it, we attached ∞ to L to obtain the generalized circle $L \cup \{\infty\}$ in $\widehat{\mathbb{C}}$. On the

Riemann sphere the point N fills the gap, so that the generalized circle $L \cup \{\infty\}$ corresponds to an actual circle. In fact, we have the following more general result, which we do not prove.

Theorem 1.4

(a) Under stereographic projection, all ordinary circles on the Riemann sphere $\mathbb{S}$ map to generalized circles in $\widehat{\mathbb{C}}$.

(b) Stereographic projection preserves angles.

Remark It can be shown that the relationship between a point $(u, v, s) \neq (0, 0, 1)$ on $\mathbb{S}$ and its image $x + iy = \pi(u, v, s)$ is given by

$$\pi(u, v, s) = \left(\frac{u}{1 - s} \right) + \left(\frac{v}{1 - s} \right) i$$

and

$$\pi^{-1}(x + iy) = \left(\frac{2x}{x^2 + y^2 + 1}, \frac{2y}{x^2 + y^2 + 1}, \frac{x^2 + y^2 - 1}{x^2 + y^2 + 1} \right).$$

For example, $\pi(0, 0, -1) = 0$ and $\pi^{-1}(10i) = \left(0, \frac{20}{101}, \frac{99}{101} \right)$.

2 MÖBIUS TRANSFORMATIONS

After working through this section, you should be able to:

(a) recognize a *Möbius transformation*;

(b) invert a Möbius transformation;

(c) compose two extended Möbius transformations;

(d) determine the fixed points of an extended Möbius transformation;

(e) find the extended Möbius transformation that maps one given set of three points in $\widehat{\mathbb{C}}$ onto another.

2.1 Properties of Möbius transformations

In the previous section, you saw that the extensions of the linear functions and the reciprocal function to $\widehat{\mathbb{C}}$ map generalized circles to generalized circles. In this section, we enlarge this class of circle-preserving functions to the so-called *Möbius transformations*.

August Ferdinand Möbius (1790–1868) was a German mathematician who worked on geometry and topology. In addition to Möbius transformations, he is remembered for his discovery of the Möbius band.

Definition A function of the form

$$f(z) = \frac{az + b}{cz + d}, \quad \text{where } a, b, c, d \in \mathbb{C} \text{ and } ad - bc \neq 0, \tag{2.1}$$

is called a **Möbius transformation**.

Möbius transformations are also known as *bilinear functions*.

Remarks

1 Every linear function is a Möbius transformation, as we can see by setting $c = 0$, $d = 1$. Also, the reciprocal function $f(z) = 1/z$ is a Möbius transformation with $a = d = 0$ and $b = c = 1$.

2 If $c = 0$, then the transformation f reduces to the function $f(z) = (a/d)z + (b/d)$, with domain $\mathbb{C}$. This is linear, because the condition $ad - bc \neq 0$ ensures that both a and d are non-zero, and so a/d is also non-zero. If $c \neq 0$, then f has domain $\mathbb{C} - \{-d/c\}$.

3 The condition that $ad - bc \neq 0$ is needed to avoid functions like

$$f(z) = \frac{6z + 4}{3z + 2},$$

where the numerator is a constant multiple of the denominator. Such functions are constant throughout their domains, and therefore fail to be conformal.

Here
$$ad - bc = (6 \times 2) - (4 \times 3)$$
$$= 0.$$

4 Notice that we can multiply the numerator and denominator of a Möbius transformation by the same non-zero constant without altering the transformation. For example, both

$$f(z) = \frac{2z + 1}{3z + 2} \quad \text{and} \quad g(z) = \frac{6z + 3}{9z + 6}$$

define the same Möbius transformation.

Problem 2.1

Which of the following functions are Möbius transformations?

(a) $f(z) = 3/z$ (b) $f(z) = (3i + 2z)/z$ (c) $f(z) = z + (3/z)$

(d) $f(z) = 1$ (e) $f(z) = (z + i)/(iz - 1)$

(f) $f(z) = (1 - i + z)/(2 + 3z)$

The Combination Rules for differentiation show that every Möbius transformation $f(z) = (az + b)/(cz + d)$ is an analytic function. Furthermore, the condition $ad - bc \neq 0$ ensures that the derivative

$$f'(z) = \frac{(cz + d)a - (az + b)c}{(cz + d)^2} = \frac{ad - bc}{(cz + d)^2}$$

is non-zero throughout the domain of f. This leads to the following theorem.

Theorem 2.1 Every Möbius transformation is analytic and conformal.

Conformality follows from *Unit A4*, Theorem 4.2.

Since any Möbius transformation f is a rational function, we can extend f to $\widehat{\mathbb{C}}$ in the manner described in Section 1. If $c = 0$, then f is a linear function and so we define the extended function $\widehat{f}$ by

$$\widehat{f}(z) = \begin{cases} f(z), & z \in \mathbb{C}, \\ \infty, & z = \infty. \end{cases}$$

However, if $c \neq 0$, then f has a pole at $-d/c$ and a removable singularity at ∞, since

$$\lim_{w \to 0} f(1/w) = a/c.$$

Thus, in this case, we define the extended function $\widehat{f}$ by

$$\widehat{f}(z) = \begin{cases} f(z), & z \in \mathbb{C} - \{-d/c\}, \\ \infty, & z = -d/c, \\ a/c, & z = \infty. \end{cases}$$

In either case, we call $\widehat{f}$ an **extended Möbius transformation**.

There is no need to remember these formulas for extending f, since it is usually just as easy to deal with each transformation by inspection as it arises.

In many texts, what we have called an extended Möbius transformation is called a Möbius transformation.

Problem 2.2

For each of the following Möbius transformations f, specify $\widehat{f}$.

(a) $f(z) = \dfrac{2z + i}{-3z + 1}$

(b) $f(z) = \dfrac{z - i}{3z + 2}$

(c) $f(z) = 2z + 1$

In order to investigate the properties of Möbius transformations, we now show that every Möbius transformation $f(z) = (az + b)/(cz + d)$ is either a linear function, or a composition of linear functions and the reciprocal function.

In fact we have already seen that such a transformation is linear if $c = 0$. If $c \neq 0$, then the Möbius transformation f can be expressed as a composition of linear functions and the reciprocal function as follows:

$$
\begin{aligned}
f(z) &= \frac{az + b}{cz + d} \\
&= \frac{a(cz + d) - ad + bc}{c(cz + d)} \\
&= -\left(\frac{ad - bc}{c}\right) \cdot \left(\frac{1}{cz + d}\right) + \frac{a}{c}.
\end{aligned}
$$

Multiply numerator and denominator by c; then add ad and subtract ad in the numerator.

So, for all z in $\mathbb{C} - \{-d/c\}$, it follows that $f(z)$ is equal to $(g \circ h \circ k)(z)$, where

$$
\begin{aligned}
k(z) &= cz + d && \text{(a linear function)}, \\
h(z) &= 1/z && \text{(reciprocal function)}, \\
g(z) &= -((ad - bc)/c)z + (a/c) && \text{(a linear function)}.
\end{aligned}
$$

Furthermore, we have

$$
\widehat{f} = \widehat{g} \circ \widehat{h} \circ \widehat{k},
$$

because

$$
(\widehat{g} \circ \widehat{h} \circ \widehat{k})(-d/c) = (\widehat{g} \circ \widehat{h})(0) = \widehat{g}(\infty) = \infty = \widehat{f}(-d/c),
$$

and

$$
(\widehat{g} \circ \widehat{h} \circ \widehat{k})(\infty) = (\widehat{g} \circ \widehat{h})(\infty) = \widehat{g}(0) = a/c = \widehat{f}(\infty).
$$

Since the extended linear functions and the extended reciprocal function map $\widehat{\mathbb{C}}$ one-one onto $\widehat{\mathbb{C}}$ and generalized circles onto generalized circles, we obtain the following result.

Theorem 1.3

Theorem 2.2 Extended Möbius transformations map

(a) $\widehat{\mathbb{C}}$ one-one onto $\widehat{\mathbb{C}}$;

(b) generalized circles onto generalized circles.

It follows from Theorem 2.2(a) that every Möbius transformation f must have an inverse function. The following example illustrates how to find such an inverse function. The method is the same as that used in *Unit A2*, except that it is now easier to check that f is one-one.

Example 2.1

Find the inverse function f^{-1} of the Möbius transformation

$$f(z) = \frac{2z + i}{-3z + 1}.$$

Check that $\widehat{f}^{-1} = \widehat{f^{-1}}$, that is, that the inverse function of the extended function associated with f is equal to the extended function associated with f^{-1}.

Solution

By Theorem 2.2, $\widehat{f}$ is a one-one function from $\widehat{\mathbb{C}}$ onto $\widehat{\mathbb{C}}$. Also $\widehat{f}(1/3) = \infty$ and $\widehat{f}(\infty) = -2/3$. So f must be a one-one function from $\mathbb{C} - \{1/3\}$ onto $\mathbb{C} - \{-2/3\}$.

Now, for each w in $\mathbb{C} - \{-2/3\}$, we need to solve the equation

$$w = \frac{2z + i}{-3z + 1}$$

to obtain the unique solution z in $\mathbb{C} - \{1/3\}$. We have

$$-3zw + w = 2z + i \quad \Longleftrightarrow \quad 3zw + 2z = w - i$$
$$\Longleftrightarrow \quad z = \frac{w - i}{3w + 2}.$$

The inverse function of the Möbius transformation f is therefore

$$f^{-1}(w) = \frac{w - i}{3w + 2} \quad (w \in \mathbb{C} - \{-2/3\}).$$

Since $\widehat{f}(\infty) = -2/3$ and $\widehat{f}(1/3) = \infty$, we have

$$\widehat{f}^{-1}(-2/3) = \infty \quad \text{and} \quad \widehat{f}^{-1}(\infty) = 1/3.$$

But $\widehat{f^{-1}}(-2/3) = \infty$ and $\widehat{f^{-1}}(\infty) = 1/3$, so that $\widehat{f}^{-1} = \widehat{f^{-1}}$, as required. ∎

Problem 2.3

For each of the following Möbius transformations f, find f^{-1} and check that $\widehat{f}^{-1} = \widehat{f^{-1}}$.

(a) $f(z) = \dfrac{z - i}{3z + 2}$ \qquad (b) $f(z) = \dfrac{z + 2i}{3z - 4}$

It appears from Example 2.1 and Problem 2.3 that the inverse function of a Möbius transformation is itself a Möbius transformation. The next theorem confirms that this is always the case.

Theorem 2.3 Inverse function of a Möbius transformation

The Möbius transformation

$$f(z) = \frac{az + b}{cz + d}, \quad \text{where } a, b, c, d \in \mathbb{C} \text{ and } ad - bc \neq 0,$$

is a one-one function from $\mathbb{C} - \{-d/c\}$ onto $\mathbb{C} - \{a/c\}$, with inverse function

$$f^{-1}(w) = \frac{dw - b}{-cw + a}.$$

Furthermore, $\widehat{f}^{-1} = \widehat{f^{-1}}$.

This theorem can be proved by the same algebraic argument as was used in Example 2.1 and Problem 2.3.

To help remember this formula for f^{-1}, compare it with the formula for the inverse of the matrix

$$M = \begin{pmatrix} a & b \\ c & d \end{pmatrix},$$

which is

$$M^{-1} = \frac{1}{ad - bc} \begin{pmatrix} d & -b \\ -c & a \end{pmatrix}.$$

Problem 2.4

Prove Theorem 2.3.

When finding the inverse function of a Möbius transformation f, you may choose to solve the equation $w = f(z)$ for z directly, as in Problem 2.3. Alternatively, you may prefer to use Theorem 2.3. Either way, it follows from the final part of Theorem 2.3 that $\widehat{f}^{-1} = \widehat{f^{-1}}$. This means that to find the inverse of an *extended* Möbius transformation $\widehat{f}$, it is sufficient to find the inverse of f. There is no need to check the singularities separately, since they are taken care of automatically by the extension of f^{-1}.

Problem 2.5

Use Theorem 2.3 to check your answers to Problem 2.3.

Since every extended Möbius transformation can be written as the composition of extended linear functions and the extended reciprocal function, it is natural to ask whether any new transformations are obtained when extended Möbius transformations are composed. The following theorem shows that the composition of two extended Möbius transformations just yields another extended Möbius transformation.

Theorem 2.4 Composition of extended Möbius transformations

If $\widehat{f}$ and $\widehat{g}$ are extended Möbius transformations, then $\widehat{g} \circ \widehat{f}$ is also an extended Möbius transformation.

Before giving a proof of this theorem, we illustrate how it can be used to find the composition of two extended Möbius transformations.

Example 2.2

Find the composition $\widehat{g} \circ \widehat{f}$, where f and g are the Möbius transformations

$$f(z) = \frac{z + i}{2z - 1} \quad \text{and} \quad g(z) = \frac{iz + 1}{2z - 2}.$$

Solution

If z belongs to the domain of $g \circ f$, then $(\widehat{g} \circ \widehat{f})(z) = (g \circ f)(z)$ and so

$$(\widehat{g} \circ \widehat{f})(z) = g\left(\frac{z + i}{2z - 1}\right)$$

$$= \frac{i\left(\dfrac{z + i}{2z - 1}\right) + 1}{2\left(\dfrac{z + i}{2z - 1}\right) - 2}$$

$$= \frac{i(z + i) + (2z - 1)}{2(z + i) - 2(2z - 1)} = \frac{(2 + i)z - 2}{-2z + (2 + 2i)}.$$

By Theorem 2.4, $\widehat{g} \circ \widehat{f}$ is an extended Möbius transformation, and so it must be the function $\widehat{h}$ where h is the Möbius transformation

$$h(z) = \frac{(2 + i)z - 2}{-2z + (2 + 2i)}. \quad \blacksquare$$

Problem 2.6

Find the composition $\widehat{g} \circ \widehat{f}$, where f and g are the Möbius transformations

$$f(z) = \frac{z + i}{z - i} \quad \text{and} \quad g(z) = \frac{z + 2}{z - 2}.$$

Proof of Theorem 2.4

Let $\widehat{f}$ and $\widehat{g}$ be extended Möbius transformations. Then, using the same algebra as in Example 2.2, we can show that $(\widehat{g} \circ \widehat{f})(z)$ has the form $(az + b)/(cz + d)$ for all z in the domain of $g \circ f$. Since $\widehat{g} \circ \widehat{f}$ is a one-one function, the function

$$h(z) = \frac{az + b}{cz + d}$$

must be non-constant, and hence is a Möbius transformation. We know that

$$(\widehat{g} \circ \widehat{f})(z) = (g \circ f)(z) = \widehat{h}(z),$$

for all z in the domain, A say, of $g \circ f$. To show that $(\widehat{g} \circ \widehat{f})(\alpha) = \widehat{h}(\alpha)$ at any singularity α (possibly ∞) of $g \circ f$, let $\{z_n\}$ be a sequence in A tending to α. Then $\widehat{h}(z_n) \to \widehat{h}(\alpha)$ (possibly ∞). Also, $\widehat{f}(z_n) \to \widehat{f}(\alpha)$ and so

$$\widehat{g}(\widehat{f}(z_n)) \to \widehat{g}(\widehat{f}(\alpha)).$$

Since $\widehat{h}(z_n) = \widehat{g}(\widehat{f}(z_n))$, it follows that $\widehat{h}(\alpha) = \widehat{g}(\widehat{f}(\alpha))$, as required. ∎

Moreover, the matrix of coefficients of h

$$\begin{pmatrix} a & b \\ c & d \end{pmatrix}$$

can be found by multiplying the matrices corresponding to f and g. For Example 2.2, we have

$$\begin{pmatrix} i & 1 \\ 2 & -2 \end{pmatrix}\begin{pmatrix} 1 & i \\ 2 & -1 \end{pmatrix}$$
$$= \begin{pmatrix} 2+i & -2 \\ -2 & 2+2i \end{pmatrix}.$$

If we compose any extended Möbius transformation $\widehat{f}$ with its inverse function $\widehat{f}^{-1}$, then we obtain a function $\widehat{f} \circ \widehat{f}^{-1}$ that maps every element of $\widehat{\mathbb{C}}$ to itself. This function is the **identity function on** $\widehat{\mathbb{C}}$. It is easy to see that this function is an extended Möbius transformation, since it can be written as $\widehat{k}$, where

$$k(z) = \frac{z + 0}{0z + 1}.$$

We now have all the properties that are needed to manipulate compositions of extended Möbius transformations. A summary of these properties is provided by the following theorem. If you have studied group theory, then you will recognize the theorem as asserting that the extended Möbius transformations form a group under composition of functions.

Theorem 2.5 Group properties

The set of extended Möbius transformations has the following properties.

Closure If $\widehat{f}$ and $\widehat{g}$ are extended Möbius transformations, then so is $\widehat{f} \circ \widehat{g}$.

Identity The identity function on $\widehat{\mathbb{C}}$ is an extended Möbius transformation.

Inverses Every extended Möbius transformation $\widehat{f}$ has an inverse function $\widehat{f}^{-1}$.

Associativity If $\widehat{f}$, $\widehat{g}$ and $\widehat{h}$ are extended Möbius transformations, then

$$\widehat{f} \circ (\widehat{g} \circ \widehat{h}) = (\widehat{f} \circ \widehat{g}) \circ \widehat{h}.$$

The only property that we have not mentioned earlier is associativity. This just says that it does not matter how we bracket the calculation of a composition of Möbius transformations. It means that we can write $\widehat{f} \circ \widehat{g} \circ \widehat{h}$, without ambiguity.

Associativity is a general property of the composition of functions.

2.2 The fixed points of a Möbius transformation

In the previous subsection you saw that the identity function on $\widehat{\mathbb{C}}$ is an extended Möbius transformation that leaves every point in $\widehat{\mathbb{C}}$ fixed. By contrast, we will now show that if $\widehat{f}$ is any extended Möbius transformation other than the identity function, then it can leave at most two points fixed.

Definition A point α in the extended complex plane $\widehat{\mathbb{C}}$ is a **fixed point** of an extended Möbius transformation $\widehat{f}$ if $\widehat{f}(\alpha) = \alpha$.

In *Unit D3*, we consider the fixed points of other functions.

If $\widehat{f}$ is the extended Möbius transformation associated with

$$f(z) = \frac{az + b}{cz + d},$$

then the number of fixed points of $\widehat{f}$ depends on the coefficients a, b, c and d.

If $c = 0$, then $\widehat{f}$ is an extended linear function and therefore has ∞ as one of its fixed points. If, in addition, $a \neq d$, then $\widehat{f}$ has one other fixed point, which is the solution of $(az + b)/d = z$.

If $c \neq 0$, then $\widehat{f}(\infty) = a/c \neq \infty$, so all the fixed points of $\widehat{f}$ must lie in $\mathbb{C}$. We can find these fixed points by solving the equation

$$\frac{az + b}{cz + d} = z,$$

that is,

$$cz^2 + (d - a)z - b = 0.$$

Since this is a quadratic equation, it has either one or two solutions in $\mathbb{C}$.

So, in general, we have the following theorem.

Theorem 2.6 An extended Möbius transformation, other than the identity function, has either one or two fixed points in $\widehat{\mathbb{C}}$.

Problem 2.7

Determine the fixed points in $\widehat{\mathbb{C}}$ of the extended Möbius transformation associated with each of the following functions f.

(a) $f(z) = \frac{1}{2}z + 1$ (b) $f(z) = \dfrac{1}{z}$.

Although Theorem 2.6 is a seemingly innocuous result, it has a number of important implications. If two extended Möbius transformations $\widehat{f}$ and $\widehat{g}$ agree on a set consisting of three or more points, then the points must be fixed points of the function $\widehat{f}^{-1} \circ \widehat{g}$. By Theorem 2.6, $\widehat{f}^{-1} \circ \widehat{g}$ must be the identity function, and so

$$\widehat{f} = \widehat{f} \circ (\widehat{f}^{-1} \circ \widehat{g}) = (\widehat{f} \circ \widehat{f}^{-1}) \circ \widehat{g} = \widehat{g}.$$

We therefore have the following theorem.

Theorem 2.7 If $\widehat{f}$ and $\widehat{g}$ are two extended Möbius transformations that agree on a set consisting of three or more points in $\widehat{\mathbb{C}}$, then $\widehat{f} = \widehat{g}$.

This theorem shows that an extended Möbius transformation is completely determined by the effect that it has on any three distinct points α, β, γ in $\widehat{\mathbb{C}}$.

Now suppose that we are given two sets $\{\alpha, \beta, \gamma\}$ and $\{\alpha', \beta', \gamma'\}$, each consisting of three distinct points of $\widehat{\mathbb{C}}$. Then it is natural to ask whether we can find an extended Möbius transformation $\widehat{f}$ that maps

$$\alpha \text{ to } \alpha', \quad \beta \text{ to } \beta' \quad \text{and} \quad \gamma \text{ to } \gamma'.$$

It turns out that we can, but rather than finding such a transformation directly, it is easier to begin by considering the case where α', β', γ' is the so-called **standard triple** of points $0, 1, \infty$, respectively. In this case, it is easy to see that if f is the Möbius transformation defined by

$$f(z) = \frac{(z - \alpha)}{(z - \gamma)} \frac{(\beta - \gamma)}{(\beta - \alpha)}, \tag{2.2}$$

then $\widehat{f}(\alpha) = 0$, $\widehat{f}(\beta) = 1$ and $\widehat{f}(\gamma) = \infty$, as required. Note that this formula for f works even when one of the points α, β, or γ is the point at infinity, provided we agree that terms containing ∞ are 'cancelled out'. For example, if $\alpha = \infty$, then the correct formula is

$$f(z) = \frac{(z - \infty)}{(z - \gamma)} \frac{(\beta - \gamma)}{(\beta - \infty)} = \frac{\beta - \gamma}{z - \gamma}.$$

Indeed, $\widehat{f}(\infty) = 0$, $\widehat{f}(\beta) = 1$ and $\widehat{f}(\gamma) = \infty$, as required. A similar approach works if $\beta = \infty$ or $\gamma = \infty$.

Notice that the numerator cannot be a non-zero multiple of the denominator, since α, β and γ are distinct, and so f is a Möbius transformation.

Example 2.3

For each of the triples below, use Formula (2.2) to find the extended Möbius transformation that sends the three points to the standard triple $0, 1, \infty$, respectively.

(a) $i, 1, -i$ (b) $2, \infty, 1 + i$

Solution

(a) By Formula (2.2), the transformation is $\widehat{f}$, where

$$f(z) = \frac{(z - i)}{(z + i)} \frac{(1 + i)}{(1 - i)} = \frac{(z - i)}{(z + i)}(i) = \frac{iz + 1}{z + i}.$$

(b) Here the transformation is $\widehat{f}$, where

$$f(z) = \frac{(z - 2)}{(z - (1 + i))} \frac{(\infty - (1 + i))}{(\infty - 2)} = \frac{z - 2}{z - (1 + i)}. \quad \blacksquare$$

Problem 2.8

For each of the triples below, find the extended Möbius transformation that sends the three points to the standard triple $0, 1, \infty$, respectively.

(a) $2, 2i, -2$ (b) $i, \infty, 1$ (c) $\infty, 3i, 1$ (d) $1 + i, 0, \infty$

With a little practice you can write down the Möbius transformation without reference to Formula (2.2). You just need to remember that for α to be mapped to 0, we need $z - \alpha$ in the numerator and for γ to be mapped to ∞, we need $z - \gamma$ in the denominator. Then you simply multiply by the quantity which yields 1 when β is substituted for z.

In Example 2.3(a), the stages are:

$$z - i, \quad \frac{z - i}{z + i},$$

$$\frac{z - i}{z + i}\left(\frac{1 + i}{1 - i}\right).$$

Let us now return to the question that we posed earlier about whether, given two triples of distinct points α, β, γ and α', β', γ', there is an extended Möbius transformation which maps α, β, γ to α', β', γ', respectively.

We can construct such a transformation, by going via the standard triple of points $0, 1, \infty$. We know that there is a transformation $\widehat{f}$ that sends the triple α, β, γ to the standard triple $0, 1, \infty$, respectively. Similarly, there is another transformation $\widehat{g}$ that sends the triple α', β', γ' to the standard triple $0, 1, \infty$, respectively. It follows that the composite $\widehat{g}^{-1} \circ \widehat{f}$ must be the required extended Möbius transformation, since it sends the points α, β, γ to the points α', β', γ', respectively (see Figure 2.1).

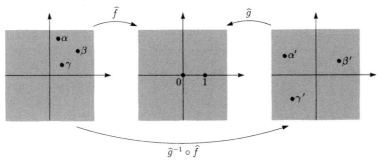

Figure 2.1

In fact, by Theorem 2.7, we know that $\widehat{g}^{-1} \circ \widehat{f}$ is the *only* such Möbius transformation, so we have established the following theorem.

Theorem 2.8 Given three distinct points α, β, γ in $\widehat{\mathbb{C}}$, and any other three distinct points α', β', γ' in $\widehat{\mathbb{C}}$, there is a unique extended Möbius transformation that maps

$$\alpha \text{ to } \alpha', \quad \beta \text{ to } \beta' \quad \text{and} \quad \gamma \text{ to } \gamma'.$$

The argument used to establish this theorem suggests that if we need to find the extended Möbius transformation that sends the points α, β, γ to the points α', β', γ', respectively, then we must write down the functions $\widehat{f}$ and $\widehat{g}$, find the inverse of $\widehat{g}$, and finally form the composite $\widehat{g}^{-1} \circ \widehat{f}$. In fact, there is a slightly simpler approach that enables us to carry out the whole calculation in one go. All we have to do is solve the equation $\widehat{f}(z) = \widehat{g}(w)$ for w in terms of z. By Formula (2.2), we need to solve

$$\frac{(z-\alpha)}{(z-\gamma)} \frac{(\beta-\gamma)}{(\beta-\alpha)} = \frac{(w-\alpha')}{(w-\gamma')} \frac{(\beta'-\gamma')}{(\beta'-\alpha')}. \tag{2.3}$$

To see this, label the left-hand plane in Figure 2.1 the z-plane and the right-hand plane the w-plane.

Equation (2.3) is known as the **Implicit Formula**.

Example 2.4

Find the extended Möbius transformation which sends the points $-i$, -1, i to the points 4, 3, 2, respectively.

Solution

We find the transformation by using the Implicit Formula, that is, by solving the equation

$$\frac{(z+i)}{(z-i)} \frac{(-1-i)}{(-1+i)} = \frac{(w-4)}{(w-2)} \frac{(3-2)}{(3-4)}.$$

By evaluating the constant terms and cross-multiplying, we obtain

$$(z+i)(w-2)(i) = (w-4)(z-i)(-1),$$

that is,

$$zwi - w - 2iz + 2 = -wz + 4z + iw - 4i.$$

On collecting the w terms on the left, we obtain

$$w(i+1)z - w(1+i) = (4+2i)z - (2+4i),$$

and so

$$w = \frac{(4+2i)z - (2+4i)}{(1+i)z - (1+i)}.$$

The required extended transformation is therefore $\widehat{f}$, where

$$f(z) = \frac{(4+2i)z - (2+4i)}{(1+i)z - (1+i)}. \quad \blacksquare$$

You may like to check that $f(-i) = 4$, $f(-1) = 3$ and $f(i) = 2$.

Problem 2.9

Find the extended Möbius transformation that sends the points 2, $2i$, -2 to the points i, ∞, 1, respectively.

Compared with the work needed to write down a Möbius transformation that sends three distinct points to the standard triple of points 0, 1 and ∞, the more general calculation, illustrated by Example 2.4 and Problem 2.9, often involves a lot more arithmetic. Fortunately, as you will see in Section 4, it is often possible to tackle conformal mapping problems in a way that uses the standard triple of points.

We end this section with the following important consequence of Theorem 2.8.

Theorem 2.9 If C_1 and C_2 are generalized circles, then there is an extended Möbius transformation that maps C_1 onto C_2.

Proof Let α, β, γ be any three distinct points on C_1 and let α', β', γ', be any three distinct points on C_2. By Theorem 2.8, there is an extended Möbius transformation $\widehat{f}$ that maps α, β, γ to α', β', γ', respectively. Since C_1 passes through α, β, γ, it follows that $\widehat{f}(C_1)$ passes through α', β', γ'. But $\widehat{f}$ preserves generalized circles and so $\widehat{f}(C_1)$ is a generalized circle that passes through α', β', γ'. Since a generalized circle is completely determined by any three of its points, it follows that $\widehat{f}(C_1) = C_2$. ∎

3 IMAGES OF GENERALIZED CIRCLES

After working through this section, you should be able to:

(a) find the image of a generalized circle by using three of its points;

(b) use *inverse points* to find the image of a generalized circle in *Apollonian form*;

(c) find the centre and radius of a circle in Apollonian form;

(d) find inverse points for a given generalized circle.

3.1 The three-point trick

In the previous section we showed that extended Möbius transformations preserve generalized circles. However, apart from the special cases of the linear and reciprocal functions, we have not yet found the image of a generalized circle under an extended Möbius transformation.

For the reciprocal function, we were able to use Cartesian coordinates to find the image of a generalized circle, but if this approach is used for a general Möbius transformation then the resulting algebra can be rather unpleasant.

An alternative approach depends on the fact that every generalized circle is completely determined by the positions of any three of its points. So, to find the image of a generalized circle C under an extended Möbius transformation $\widehat{f}$, it is sufficient to find the images of just three distinct points that lie on C.

If L is a line in $\mathbb{C}$, then the generalized circle $L \cup \{\infty\}$ can be specified by ∞ and two other points.

Example 3.1

Find the image of the circle $\{z : |z - i| = 1\}$ under the extended Möbius transformation $\widehat{f}$, where

$$f(z) = \frac{z - 2i}{z - 2}.$$

Solution

We first pick three distinct points on the circle $\{z : |z - i| = 1\}$. There is no definite rule about which points should be chosen, so, to keep the calculations simple, we pick the points 0, $1 + i$ and $2i$ (see Figure 3.1). Now

$$\widehat{f}(0) = i, \quad \widehat{f}(1 + i) = \frac{1 - i}{-1 + i} = -1 \quad \text{and} \quad \widehat{f}(2i) = 0.$$

So the image of $\{z : |z - i| = 1\}$ is the generalized circle that passes through the points i, -1 and 0. From Figure 3.1, it is evident that this is the circle of radius $1/\sqrt{2}$, centred at $(-1 + i)/2$.

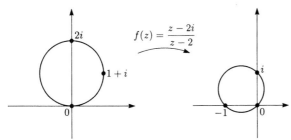

Figure 3.1

Thus, the image is the circle

$$\left\{ z : \left| z - \tfrac{1}{2}(-1 + i) \right| = 1/\sqrt{2} \right\}. \quad \blacksquare$$

Remark   Note that $f(i) = -i/(i - 2) = (-1 + 2i)/5$, so the image of the centre is *not* the centre of the image.

Problem 3.1 _____

Find the image of the circle $\{z : |z - (1 + i)| = \sqrt{2}\}$ under the extended Möbius transformation $\widehat{f}$, where

$$f(z) = \frac{-z + 2}{z + 2}.$$

Exactly the same method can be used to find the image of an extended line. Indeed, an extended line is just a special type of generalized circle and so the image can again be found by locating the images of three of its points. Any three points can be used, but the inclusion of the point at infinity often simplifies the calculation, as illustrated in the following example.

Example 3.2

Find the image of the extended real axis $\{z : \operatorname{Im} z = 0\} \cup \{\infty\}$ under the extended Möbius transformation $\widehat{f}$, where

$$f(z) = \frac{z - i}{z + i}.$$

Solution

To keep the calculations simple we pick the points 0, 1 and ∞ on the extended real axis (see Figure 3.2). Then

$$\widehat{f}(0) = -1, \quad \widehat{f}(1) = (1 - i)/(1 + i) = -i \quad \text{and} \quad \widehat{f}(\infty) = 1.$$

So the image of the extended real axis is the generalized circle that passes through the points -1, $-i$ and 1.

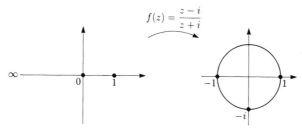

Figure 3.2

Note that, on figures, we normally specify the Möbius transformation f, even when we have considered images of points, including ∞, under $\widehat{f}$.

Thus, the image is the unit circle $\{z : |z| = 1\}$. ■

Problem 3.2

Find the image of the extended line $L = \{z : \operatorname{Re} z = \operatorname{Im} z\} \cup \{\infty\}$ under the extended Möbius transformation $\widehat{f}$, where

$$f(z) = \frac{z + i}{z - i}.$$

The three-point trick worked well in these examples because, once we had found the three image points, the image of the generalized circle was evident. Usually, however, we would not be so lucky, although careful choice of the three points may help. For example, if a pole of f lies on the circle, then the image will be an extended line, as in the following problem.

Problem 3.3

Find the image of the unit circle $C = \{z : |z| = 1\}$ under the extended Möbius transformation $\widehat{f}$, where $f(z) = \frac{z + 1}{z - 1}$.

3.2 Inverse points

We now describe a method of finding the image of a generalized circle under an extended Möbius transformation which involves the image of just one point on the circle, together with the image of two other points known as *inverse points*. The definition of these inverse points is closely related to a description of generalized circles known as *Apollonian form*. This is the form which appears when we try to find the image under $\widehat{f}$ of a circle C by substituting $z = f^{-1}(w)$ into the equation of C, as illustrated in the following example.

Example 3.3

Find an equation for the image of the unit circle $C = \{z : |z| = 1\}$ under the extended Möbius transformation $\widehat{f}$, where

$$f(z) = \frac{iz + i}{-z + 1},$$

by substituting $z = f^{-1}(w)$ into the equation of C.

Solution

By Theorem 2.3,

$$f^{-1}(w) = \frac{w - i}{w + i}.$$

So, w is a point on the image $\widehat{f}(C)$ if and only if $\widehat{f}^{-1}(w)$ lies on the unit circle C, that is, if and only if either $w = \infty$ or

Here $\widehat{f}^{-1}(\infty) = 1$.

$$\left| \frac{w - i}{w + i} \right| = 1.$$

An equation for the 'finite' points of the image is therefore

$$|w - i| = |w + i|. \quad \blacksquare$$

The equation obtained in this example represents the real axis, for it asserts that the 'finite' points of the image are equidistant from i and $-i$. The only generalized circle whose finite points fit this description is the extended real axis (see Figure 3.3).

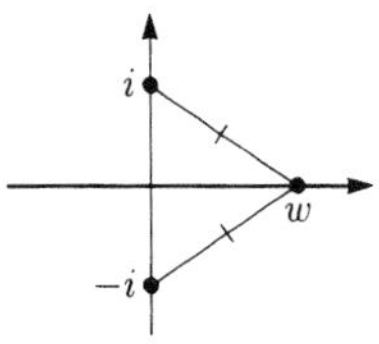

Figure 3.3

In general, given any two points α and β in $\mathbb{C}$, the equation

$$|z - \alpha| = |z - \beta|$$

describes the line L that forms the perpendicular bisector of the line segment joining α and β (see Figure 3.4).

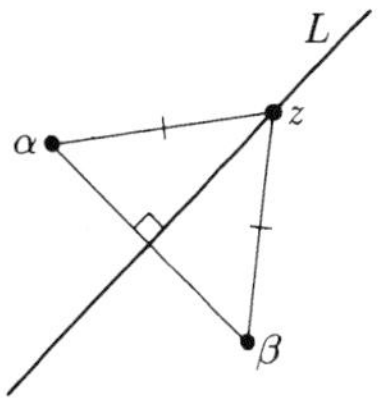

Conversely, any line L can be described by an equation of the form $|z - \alpha| = |z - \beta|$, where α and β are mirror images of each other in the line. The equation is not unique, since any pair of mirror images can be used to set up the equation.

Figure 3.4

Problem 3.4 _____

Find an equation for the image of the unit circle $C = \{z : |z| = 1\}$ under the extended Möbius transformation $\widehat{f}$, where

$$f(z) = \frac{z - i}{z + 1},$$

by substituting $z = f^{-1}(w)$ into the equation of C.

In the next example, we see what happens if the image is a circle.

Example 3.4

Find an equation for the image of the unit circle $C = \{z : |z| = 1\}$ under the extended Möbius transformation $\widehat{f}$, where

$$f(z) = \frac{6z - 2i}{2z - 1}.$$

Solution

By Theorem 2.3,

$$f^{-1}(w) = \frac{-w + 2i}{-2w + 6}.$$

So, w is a point on the image $\widehat{f}(C)$ if and only if $\widehat{f}^{-1}(w)$ lies on the unit circle C; that is, if and only if

$$\left| \frac{-w + 2i}{-2w + 6} \right| = 1.$$

An equation for the image is therefore

$$|-w + 2i| = |-2w + 6|,$$

which can be rewritten as

$$|w - 2i| = 2|w - 3|. \quad \blacksquare$$

The equation obtained in this example is similar to the equation obtained in Example 3.3. The main difference is the factor 2 that appears in front of the modulus sign on the right. This means that instead of describing a line, the equation describes the set of points that lie twice as far from $2i$ as they do from 3 (see Figure 3.5). Because f is a Möbius transformation, we know that this set must be a circle!

In general, if the method of Example 3.3 is used to find the image of an arbitrary generalized circle under an extended Möbius transformation, then it turns out that the resulting equation for the image has the form

$$|z - \alpha| = k|z - \beta|, \quad \text{where } k > 0. \tag{3.1}$$

Generalized circles that are presented in this form are said to be expressed in **Apollonian form**. The form describes the set of points that lie k times as far from α as they do from β. If $k = 1$, then we shall adopt the convention that ∞ is included in the set.

If $k = 1$ then, as noted earlier, the Apollonian form describes an extended line in which α and β are mirror images. But why does the form describe a circle if $k \neq 1$, and where is the centre of the circle? To answer such questions it is convenient to introduce a generalization of 'mirror images' that can be applied to arbitrary generalized circles.

We can find a suitable generalization by reformulating what it means for two points to be mirror images of each other. Suppose that α and β are mirror images of each other in an extended line L. Then either α and β are equal and lie on L, or L has an Apollonian equation $|z - \alpha| = |z - \beta|$. Now, if

$$f(z) = \frac{z - \alpha}{z - \beta},$$

then the Apollonian equation can be written in the form $|\widehat{f}(z)| = 1$. But this shows that $\widehat{f}$ maps L onto the unit circle. Furthermore, the mirror images α and β are mapped by $\widehat{f}$ to 0 and ∞, respectively. This suggests the following generalization of 'mirror images' known as *inverse points*.

In this case, $w \in \widehat{f}(C)$ cannot be ∞ since $\widehat{f}^{-1}(\infty) = \frac{1}{2}$, which does not lie on the unit circle.

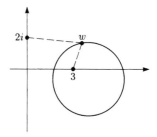

Figure 3.5

Apollonius of Perga (*c.* 260–190 BC) was noted for his study of conics. In particular, he showed that any conic can be formed by different sections of a circular conical surface and he introduced the words 'ellipse', 'parabola' and 'hyperbola'.

> **Definition** Let C be a generalized circle. Then α and β are **inverse points with respect to C** if
>
> EITHER α and β are equal and lie on C
>
> OR there exists an extended Möbius transformation $\widehat{f}$ that maps α to 0, β to ∞, and C to the unit circle.

This definition is rather unsatisfactory as it stands, because it does not give us any geometric picture of the relationship between the inverse points α and β and the generalized circle C. We shall obtain such a picture shortly, but first we establish the close connection between the inverse points and Apollonian form.

See Figure 3.6.

> **Theorem 3.1** The points α and β in $\widehat{\mathbb{C}}$ are distinct inverse points with respect to a generalized circle C if and only if
>
> EITHER both α and $\beta \in \mathbb{C}$, and C has the equation
>
> $$|z - \alpha| = k|z - \beta|, \qquad \text{for some } k > 0;$$
>
> OR one of the points (β say) is ∞, and C has the equation
>
> $$|z - \alpha| = r, \qquad \text{for some } r > 0.$$

Proof First suppose that α and β are distinct inverse points with respect to a generalized circle C. Then, by definition, there is an extended Möbius transformation $\widehat{f}$ which maps α to 0, β to ∞ and C to the unit circle. Let γ be the point on C which maps to 1. Since $\widehat{f}$ is completely determined by the effect that it has on α, β and γ, we have

$$f(z) = \frac{(z - \alpha)}{(z - \beta)} \frac{(\gamma - \beta)}{(\gamma - \alpha)},$$

with the usual rules about 'cancelling terms involving ∞'. But $\widehat{f}$ maps C onto the unit circle, so the equation of C is $|\widehat{f}(z)| = 1$, that is,

$$\left| \frac{(z - \alpha)}{(z - \beta)} \frac{(\gamma - \beta)}{(\gamma - \alpha)} \right| = 1.$$

If $\alpha, \beta \in \mathbb{C}$, then this becomes

$$\left| \frac{z - \alpha}{z - \beta} \right| = k, \qquad \text{where } k = \left| \frac{\gamma - \alpha}{\gamma - \beta} \right| > 0.$$

But if $\beta = \infty$, then the $(\gamma - \beta)$ term cancels with the $(z - \beta)$ term to give

$$|z - \alpha| = r, \qquad \text{where } r = |\gamma - \alpha| > 0.$$

Conversely, if C has equation $|z - \alpha| = k|z - \beta|$, with $k > 0$, then $\alpha \neq \beta$ and we can define

$$f(z) = \frac{1}{k}\left(\frac{z - \alpha}{z - \beta} \right),$$

whereas, if C has equation $|z - \alpha| = r$ and $\beta = \infty$, then we can define

$$f(z) = (z - \alpha)/r.$$

In either case, $\widehat{f}$ maps α to 0, β to ∞ and C to the unit circle (since $|\widehat{f}(z)| = 1$), so α and β are inverse points with respect to the generalized circle C. ∎

This proof may be omitted on a first reading.

Since α and β are distinct, they cannot lie on C. It follows that γ cannot be equal to α or β.

If C is an ordinary circle centred at α and $\beta = \infty$, then C has equation $|z - \alpha| = r$, for some r. It follows, from Theorem 3.1, that α and ∞ are inverse points with respect to C. Thus it is easy to identify at least one pair of inverse points of an ordinary circle.

Corollary If α is the centre of a circle C, then α and ∞ are inverse points with respect to C.

The next theorem provides an insight into why Möbius transformations do not preserve centres of circles. It is because the centre of any circle, together with the point at infinity, is just one of many pairs of inverse points. Möbius transformations preserve inverse pairs, not centres.

Theorem 3.2 Let $\widehat{f}$ be an extended Möbius transformation. If α and β are inverse points with respect to the generalized circle C, then $\widehat{f}(\alpha)$ and $\widehat{f}(\beta)$ are inverse points with respect to $\widehat{f}(C)$.

Proof If α and β are distinct inverse points with respect to the generalized circle C, then there must be an extended Möbius transformation $\widehat{g}$ that maps α to 0, β to ∞, and C to the unit circle. Thus $\widehat{g} \circ \widehat{f^{-1}}$ maps $\widehat{f}(\alpha)$ to 0, $\widehat{f}(\beta)$ to ∞ and $\widehat{f}(C)$ to the unit circle. It follows that $\widehat{f}(\alpha)$ and $\widehat{f}(\beta)$ are inverse points with respect to $\widehat{f}(C)$.

On the other hand, if $\alpha = \beta \in C$, then $\widehat{f}(\alpha) = \widehat{f}(\beta) \in \widehat{f}(C)$ and so once again $\widehat{f}(\alpha)$ and $\widehat{f}(\beta)$ are inverse points with respect to $\widehat{f}(C)$. ∎

We can use Theorem 3.2 to provide us with our alternative method of finding the image of a generalized circle C under an extended Möbius transformation. The method is particularly useful because, when C is an ordinary circle, it enables us to use the centre of C.

Example 3.5

Find an equation for the image of the circle $C = \{z : |z - 2i| = 3\}$ under the extended Möbius transformation $\widehat{f}$, where
$$f(z) = \frac{iz + 5}{z + i}.$$

Solution

Since C has centre $2i$, it follows from the corollary to Theorem 3.1 that $2i$ and ∞ are inverse points with respect to C. But
$$\widehat{f}(2i) = 3/3i = -i \quad \text{and} \quad \widehat{f}(\infty) = i.$$

So, by Theorem 3.2, $-i$ and i must be inverse points with respect to $\widehat{f}(C)$.

By Theorem 3.1, $\widehat{f}(C)$ has an equation of the form
$$|w - i| = k|w + i|, \quad \text{for some } k > 0.$$

But, since $5i$ lies on C, it follows that $\widehat{f}(5i) = 0$ lies on $\widehat{f}(C)$, so
$$k = \frac{|0 - i|}{|0 + i|} = 1.$$

Choosing the point $5i$ on C makes the calculation simple.

It follows that $\widehat{f}(C)$ is the extended real axis
$$\{w : |w - i| = |w + i|\}. \quad ∎$$

The same method can be used to find the equation for the image of any circle C. The resulting equation for the image of C is normally in Apollonian form, but if one of the inverse points of C maps to ∞, and the other maps to α say, then the equation will have the form $\{z : |z - \alpha| = r\}$. In such cases the value of r can be evaluated, in the same way as k, by substituting a point from the image into the equation.

Problem 3.5

For each of the following circles C, find the image of C under the extended Möbius transformation $\widehat{f}$, where

$$f(z) = \frac{z-1}{z-i}.$$

Give your answer in Apollonian form, where appropriate.

(a) $C = \{z : |z - (i+1)| = \sqrt{2}\}$
(b) $C = \{z : |z - 1| = 1\}$
(c) $C = \{z : |z - i| = 1\}$
(d) $C = \{z : |z - (i+1)| = 1\}$

Because the method usually yields the equation for the image in Apollonian form, we still may not know where the centre of the image is located. The next theorem can be used to find the centre and radius of any circle written in Apollonian form.

Theorem 3.3 Let C be the generalized circle with equation

$$|z - \alpha| = k|z - \beta|, \quad \text{where } \alpha, \beta \in \mathbb{C} \text{ and } k > 0.$$

(a) If $k \neq 1$, then C is the circle with centre λ and radius r, where

$$\lambda = \frac{\alpha - k^2 \beta}{1 - k^2} \quad \text{and} \quad r = \frac{k|\alpha - \beta|}{|1 - k^2|}. \tag{3.2}$$

Also, λ lies on the line through α and β, and

$$(\alpha - \lambda)(\overline{\beta - \lambda}) = r^2. \tag{3.3}$$

(b) If $k = 1$, then C is the line through $\frac{1}{2}(\alpha + \beta)$ perpendicular to $\beta - \alpha$.

Equation (3.3) can be rearranged as

$$\alpha - \lambda = \left|\frac{r}{\beta - \lambda}\right|^2 (\beta - \lambda).$$

Figure 3.6 $\quad |\alpha - \lambda||\beta - \lambda| = r^2$

Theorem 3.3(a) provides us with the geometric interpretation of inverse points that we promised earlier. It tells us that the centre λ of C lies on the line through α and β. Furthermore, from Equation (3.3), we have

$$|\alpha - \lambda||\beta - \lambda| = |(\alpha - \lambda)(\overline{\beta - \lambda})|$$
$$= r^2.$$

So the product of the distances of α and β from the centre of C is equal to the square of the radius of C (see Figure 3.6).

In the special case where C is the unit circle $|z| = 1$, we have $\alpha \overline{\beta} = 1$, that is, $\alpha = 1/\overline{\beta}$. So α is the reciprocal of the mirror image of β in the real axis (see Figure 3.7). The function $f(z) = 1/\overline{z}$, which sends β to α here is known as **inversion**. It differs from the reciprocal function in that inversion, like reflection, is not analytic.

Before proving Theorem 3.3, we ask you to use it in the following problem.

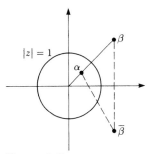

Figure 3.7

Problem 3.6

Determine the centres and radii of the image circles in Problem 3.5(a) and (b).

Proof of Theorem 3.3

Let f be the Möbius transformation defined by

$$f(z) = \frac{1}{k}\left(\frac{z - \alpha}{z - \beta}\right) = \frac{z - \alpha}{kz - k\beta}.$$

This proof may be omitted on a first reading.

Then $\widehat{f}$ maps C to the unit circle, and so $\widehat{f}^{-1}$ maps the unit circle to C. Furthermore, by Theorem 2.3,

$$f^{-1}(w) = \frac{-k\beta w + \alpha}{-kw + 1},$$

and so

$$\widehat{f}^{-1}(0) = \alpha, \quad \widehat{f}^{-1}(1/k) = \infty \quad \text{and} \quad \widehat{f}^{-1}(\infty) = \beta.$$

Since $1/k$ is a real number, points on the extended real axis are mapped by $\widehat{f}^{-1}$ to points on the extended line L through α and β.

(a) If $k \neq 1$, then the diametrically opposite points -1 and 1 must be mapped by $\widehat{f}^{-1}$ to the diametrically opposite points of C on L, because f^{-1} is conformal at 1 and -1 (see Figure 3.8). These points are

$$\widehat{f}^{-1}(-1) = \frac{\alpha + k\beta}{1 + k} \quad \text{and} \quad \widehat{f}^{-1}(1) = \frac{\alpha - k\beta}{1 - k}.$$

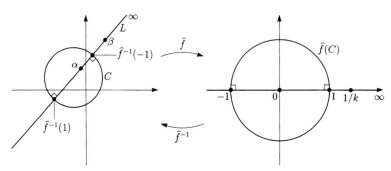

Figure 3.8 The case $0 < k < 1$

It follows that C has centre λ on L given by

$$\lambda = \frac{1}{2}\left(\frac{\alpha + k\beta}{1 + k} + \frac{\alpha - k\beta}{1 - k}\right) = \frac{\alpha - k^2\beta}{1 - k^2},$$

and radius r given by

$$r = \frac{1}{2}\left|\frac{\alpha + k\beta}{1 + k} - \frac{\alpha - k\beta}{1 - k}\right| = \frac{k|\alpha - \beta|}{|1 - k^2|}.$$

Furthermore,

$$\begin{aligned}
(\alpha - \lambda)(\overline{\beta - \lambda}) &= \left(\alpha - \frac{\alpha - k^2\beta}{1 - k^2}\right)\overline{\left(\beta - \frac{\alpha - k^2\beta}{1 - k^2}\right)} \\
&= \left(\frac{k^2(\beta - \alpha)}{1 - k^2}\right)\overline{\left(\frac{\beta - \alpha}{1 - k^2}\right)} \\
&= \left(\frac{k|\alpha - \beta|}{|1 - k^2|}\right)^2 \\
&= r^2,
\end{aligned}$$

as required.

(b) If $k = 1$, then $\widehat{f}^{-1}(1) = \infty$, and so C must be a line that meets L in a right angle at the point

$$\widehat{f}^{-1}(-1) = \frac{(-1)\cdot\beta\cdot(-1) + \alpha}{(-1)\cdot(-1) + 1} = \tfrac{1}{2}(\alpha + \beta). \quad \blacksquare$$

Any circle has infinitely many pairs of inverse points, as the following theorem shows.

Theorem 3.4 Existence of inverse points

Let C be a generalized circle and let β be an arbitrary point of $\widehat{\mathbb{C}}$. Then β has a unique inverse point α with respect to C.

Proof If $\beta \in C$, then we take $\alpha = \beta$, as in the first part of the definition of inverse points with respect to C. Otherwise, let L be the extended line through β that meets C at right angles at the point λ_1 (see Figure 3.9). If C is a circle, then L is the line through the centre of C and it meets C again at the diametrically opposite point λ_2. On the other hand, if C is an extended line, then L meets C again at $\lambda_2 = \infty$.

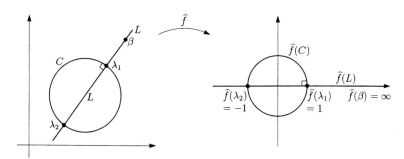

Figure 3.9

In either case, let $\widehat{f}$ be the extended Möbius transformation that maps β to ∞, λ_1 to 1 and λ_2 to -1. Then $\widehat{f}(L)$ is the extended real axis and it meets $\widehat{f}(C)$ at $\widehat{f}(\lambda_1) = 1$ and $\widehat{f}(\lambda_2) = -1$. Furthermore, the angle of intersection at $\widehat{f}(\lambda_1)$ is a right angle, so $\widehat{f}(C)$ must be the unit circle. Now if $\alpha = \widehat{f}^{-1}(0)$, then $\widehat{f}(\alpha) = 0$ and $\widehat{f}(\beta) = \infty$, and so α and β are inverse points with respect to C.

Finally, note that since α and β are inverse points with respect to C, an Apollonian form for C is $|z - \alpha| = k|z - \beta|$, where $k > 0$, and so α must be unique, by Theorem 3.3. ∎

So, given any generalized circle C and any point β, there is a point α such that α and β are inverse points with respect to C. Furthermore, we can find the point α that is inverse to β by using Theorems 3.1 and 3.3.

Example 3.6

Determine the point α such that α and $\beta = 1 + 2i$ are inverse points with respect to the circle $C = \{z : |z - i| = 2\}$. Hence write down an equation for C in Apollonian form.

Solution

Here C has centre i and radius 2, so $\lambda = i$ and $r = 2$. Thus, by Equation (3.3),

$$\alpha - i = 2^2/(\overline{\beta - i}) = 4/(\overline{1 + i}) = 4(1 + i)/2 = 2 + 2i.$$

Thus $\alpha = 2 + 3i$, and so C has an equation of the form

$$|z - (2 + 3i)| = k|z - (1 + 2i)|,$$

where, since $-i$ lies on C,

$$k = \frac{|-i - (2 + 3i)|}{|-i - (1 + 2i)|} = \frac{|-2 - 4i|}{|-1 - 3i|} = \frac{\sqrt{20}}{\sqrt{10}} = \sqrt{2},$$

that is, an equation for C is

$$|z - (2 + 3i)| = \sqrt{2}|z - (1 + 2i)|. \blacksquare$$

Problem 3.7

Determine the point α such that α and $\beta = 1 + i$ are inverse points with respect to the circle $C = \{z : |z - 2| = 1\}$. Hence write down an equation for C in Apollonian form.

In the case of an extended line the inverse points can be found by reflection.

Example 3.7

Determine the point α such that α and i are inverse points with respect to the extended line $L = \{z : \operatorname{Re} z = \operatorname{Im} z\} \cup \{\infty\}$. Hence write down an equation for L in Apollonian form.

Solution

The reflection of the point i in L is 1, and so, by Theorem 3.3(b), $\alpha = 1$ (see Figure 3.10). An equation for L is therefore

$$|z - 1| = |z - i|. \quad \blacksquare$$

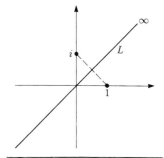

Figure 3.10

Problem 3.8

For each of the following points β, determine the point α such that α and β are inverse points with respect to the given extended line L. Hence write down an equation for L in Apollonian form.

(a) $\beta = 2 + 3i$; L is the extended imaginary axis.

(b) $\beta = 4 - 2i$; $L = \{z : \operatorname{Re} z = 3\} \cup \{\infty\}$.

(c) $\beta = 2i$; $L = \{z : \operatorname{Re} z = \operatorname{Im} z\} \cup \{\infty\}$.

Finally, we remark (but do not prove) that if α and β are inverse points with respect to a generalized circle C, then every circle through α and β meets C at right angles (see Figure 3.11, which shows the special case when C is an extended line).

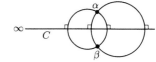

Figure 3.11

4 TRANSFORMING REGIONS

After working through this section, you should be able to:

(a) write down the *boundary in* $\widehat{\mathbb{C}}$ of a set which lies in $\widehat{\mathbb{C}}$;

(b) find the image of a *generalized open disc* under an extended Möbius transformation;

(c) construct an extended Möbius transformation which sends a generalized open disc onto the open unit disc;

(d) construct an extended Möbius transformation which sends a generalized open disc onto a given open half-plane;

(e) construct simple composite mappings which send one given region onto another;

(f) understand the definitions of the inverse sin and tan functions and the *Joukowski function*.

4.1 Images of generalized discs

So far we have concentrated on finding the images of generalized circles under extended Möbius transformations. However, one of the main objectives of the unit is to investigate the effect that conformal mappings have on regions. We begin this investigation by describing how to find the image of a region under a Möbius transformation. The technique is to find the image of the boundary of the region and use this to determine the image of the region itself.

First we need to generalize the definition of 'boundary' that we gave in *Unit A3*, Section 5 to make it applicable to sets in the extended complex plane. We do this by introducing the idea of an **open disc centred at** ∞. Such a set has the form $\{z : |z| > M\} \cup \{\infty\}$, where $M > 0$, and on the Riemann sphere $\mathbb{S}$ it corresponds to a cap-shaped disc, centred at the North Pole (see Figure 4.1). This enables us to make the following definition.

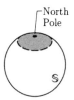

Figure 4.1

Definition Let A be a subset of $\widehat{\mathbb{C}}$ and let $\alpha \in \widehat{\mathbb{C}}$. Then α is a **boundary point in** $\widehat{\mathbb{C}}$ of A if each open disc centred at α contains at least one point of A and at least one point of $\widehat{\mathbb{C}} - A$.

The set of boundary points in $\widehat{\mathbb{C}}$ of A forms the **boundary in** $\widehat{\mathbb{C}}$ of A.

If A is a bounded set, then the boundary in $\widehat{\mathbb{C}}$ of A is the same as the boundary of A. For example, the boundary in $\widehat{\mathbb{C}}$ of the open unit disc is the unit circle.

For a set that is not bounded, we must also check whether the point at infinity lies on the boundary in $\widehat{\mathbb{C}}$. For example, the boundary in $\widehat{\mathbb{C}}$ of the upper half-plane $\{z : \operatorname{Im} z > 0\}$ includes ∞ because every open disc of the form $\{z : |z| > M\} \cup \{\infty\}$ centred at ∞ includes both points like $2Mi$, which belong to the upper half-plane, and points like $-2Mi$ which do not (see Figure 4.2).

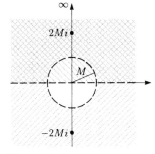

Figure 4.2

Problem 4.1 _____

Write down the boundary in $\widehat{\mathbb{C}}$ of each of the following subsets of $\widehat{\mathbb{C}}$.

(a) $\{z : |z| < 2\}$ (b) $\{z : \operatorname{Re} z < 1\}$

(c) $\{z : |z| > 3\} \cup \{\infty\}$ (d) $\{z : |z| > 3\}$

The sets in parts (a), (b) and (c) of Problem 4.1 have boundaries in $\widehat{\mathbb{C}}$ consisting of generalized circles. Any generalized circle divides $\widehat{\mathbb{C}}$ into two parts, each of which is called a **generalized open disc**. All ordinary open discs are generalized open discs, as are open discs centred at ∞. Also, all open half-planes are generalized open discs. On the Riemann sphere generalized open discs correspond to cap-shaped discs (see Figure 4.3).

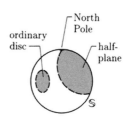

Figure 4.3

We now state the theorem which enables us to find the image of a region under a Möbius transformation f, by finding the image of its boundary under $\widehat{f}$.

Theorem 4.1 Let f be a Möbius transformation and let $\mathcal{R}$ be a region in the domain of f. Then $f(\mathcal{R})$ is a region and the extended Möbius transformation $\widehat{f}$ maps the boundary in $\widehat{\mathbb{C}}$ of $\mathcal{R}$ onto the boundary in $\widehat{\mathbb{C}}$ of $f(\mathcal{R})$.

Proof Since f is analytic and non-constant on $\mathcal{R}$ it follows from the corollary of the Open Mapping Theorem (*Unit C2*, Theorem 3.1) that $f(\mathcal{R})$ is a region.

This proof may be omitted on a first reading.

To show that $\widehat{f}$ maps the boundary in $\widehat{\mathbb{C}}$ of $\mathcal{R}$ onto the boundary in $\widehat{\mathbb{C}}$ of $f(\mathcal{R})$, we first show that if D' is any open disc in $\widehat{\mathbb{C}}$ centred at $\beta = \widehat{f}(\alpha)$, where $\alpha \in \widehat{\mathbb{C}}$, then there is an open disc D centred at α such that $\widehat{f}(D) \subseteq D'$. There are three cases:

(a) If α belongs to the domain of f, then f is continuous at α. So, for each disc $D' = \{w : |w - \beta| < \varepsilon\}$, there is a disc $D = \{z : |z - \alpha| < \delta\}$ such that $\widehat{f}(D) = f(D) \subseteq D'$.

Here D must be chosen small enough to lie in the domain of f.

(b) If $\alpha \in \mathbb{C}$ and α is a pole of f, then $f(z) \to \infty$ as $z \to \alpha$. So, for each disc $D' = \{w : |w| > M\} \cup \{\infty\}$, centred at ∞, there is a $\delta > 0$ such that

$$f(z) \in D', \quad \text{whenever } 0 < |z - \alpha| < \delta.$$

The existence of δ follows from the remark that precedes Theorem 1.1 of Unit B4.

Moreover $\widehat{f}(\alpha) = \infty$, and so $\widehat{f}(z) \in D'$ whenever $|z - \alpha| < \delta$. Thus if $D = \{z : |z - \alpha| < \delta\}$, then $\widehat{f}(D) \subseteq D'$.

(c) If $\alpha = \infty$, then f has a removable singularity or a pole at α. So, for each disc D' centred at $\beta = f(\alpha)$, there is a $\delta > 0$ such that

$$f(1/w) \in D', \quad \text{whenever } 0 < |w| < \delta.$$

Remember that the function f is defined to have a removable singularity or a pole at ∞ if the function $g(w) = f(1/w)$ has the corresponding singularity at 0.

But this means that $f(z) \in D'$, whenever $|z| > 1/\delta$, and so if D is the disc $\{z : |z| > 1/\delta\} \cup \{\infty\}$, then $\widehat{f}(D) \subseteq D'$.

Next suppose that α is a boundary point in $\widehat{\mathbb{C}}$ of $\mathcal{R}$ and let D' be any open disc centred at $\beta = f(\alpha)$. Then there is an open disc D centred at α, such that $\widehat{f}(D) \subseteq D'$. But α is a boundary point in $\widehat{\mathbb{C}}$ of $\mathcal{R}$ and so D contains points from both $\mathcal{R}$ and $\widehat{\mathbb{C}} - \mathcal{R}$. It follows that $\widehat{f}(D)$, and hence D', contains points from both $\widehat{f}(\mathcal{R}) = f(\mathcal{R})$ and $\widehat{\mathbb{C}} - f(\mathcal{R})$, and so β is a boundary point in $\widehat{\mathbb{C}}$ of $f(\mathcal{R})$.

In order to show that the mapping is *onto*, we can apply the same argument to the function $\widehat{f}^{-1}$ and hence show that if β is a boundary point in $\widehat{\mathbb{C}}$ of $f(\mathcal{R})$, then $\alpha = \widehat{f}^{-1}(\beta)$ is a boundary point in $\widehat{\mathbb{C}}$ of $\mathcal{R}$. The result follows. ∎

The next example illustrates how Theorem 4.1 can be used to determine the image of a region.

Example 4.1

Find the image of the open unit disc $D = \{z : |z| < 1\}$ under the Möbius transformation

$$f(z) = \frac{z - i}{z + 1}.$$

Solution

The boundary of D is the unit circle $C = \{z : |z| = 1\}$. By Problem 3.4, we know that the image of this circle under $\widehat{f}$ is the extended line $L = \{z : \operatorname{Re} z + \operatorname{Im} z = 0\} \cup \{\infty\}$. Neither of the singularities of f (at -1 and ∞) belongs to D and so, by Theorem 4.1 with $\mathcal{R} = D$, it follows that L is the boundary in $\widehat{\mathbb{C}}$ of the region $f(D)$.

But there are only two regions that have L as a boundary in $\widehat{\mathbb{C}}$, namely

$$\{z : \operatorname{Re} z + \operatorname{Im} z < 0\} \quad \text{and} \quad \{z : \operatorname{Re} z + \operatorname{Im} z > 0\}.$$

One way to decide which of these regions is equal to $f(D)$, is to imagine that you are walking anticlockwise around C, starting at 1, passing through i and finishing at -1. As you walk, your image walks along L, starting at $\widehat{f}(1) = (1 - i)/2$, passing through $\widehat{f}(i) = 0$ and ending at $\widehat{f}(-1) = \infty$ (see Figure 4.4).

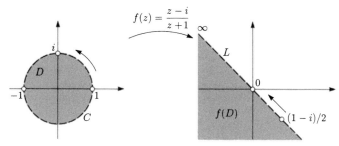

Figure 4.4

Throughout your journey around the unit circle C, the open unit disc is on your left. Since the orientation of the angle between your left-hand side and your direction of motion is preserved by f at each point of C (because f is conformal), the set $f(D)$ must be on the left of your image too. It follows that $f(D) = \{z : \operatorname{Re} z + \operatorname{Im} z < 0\}$.

An alternative approach is to pick a point in D, such as 0, and observe that $\widehat{f}(0) = -i$. Since $-i$ lies in $\{z : \operatorname{Re} z + \operatorname{Im} z < 0\}$, it follows that $f(D) = \{z : \operatorname{Re} z + \operatorname{Im} z < 0\}$. ∎

It's always useful to have a check on your working!

Problem 4.2

Find the image of the open unit disc $D = \{z : |z| < 1\}$ under the Möbius transformation

$$f(z) = \frac{z + 1}{z - 1}.$$

Use Problem 3.3.

Sometimes it is necessary to find the image under $\widehat{f}$ of a set that contains one or more singularities of f. In such cases we cannot apply Theorem 4.1 directly because f is not defined throughout the set. Fortunately we can overcome this difficulty by including the singularities as part of the boundary, as we now demonstrate.

Example 4.2

Let f be the Möbius transformation defined by

$$f(z) = \frac{iz + 5}{z + i}.$$

Find the image of the region $\mathcal{R} = \{z : |z - 2i| > 3\}$ under f, and hence find the image of the generalized open disc $D = \{z : |z - 2i| > 3\} \cup \{\infty\}$ under $\widehat{f}$.

The singularities of f are at $-i$ and ∞. D contains ∞.

Solution

The boundary in $\widehat{\mathbb{C}}$ of $\mathcal{R}$ is the set $C \cup \{\infty\}$, where C is the circle $\{z : |z - 2i| = 3\}$. In Example 3.5 we showed that the image of C under $\widehat{f}$ is the extended real axis. Also, $\widehat{f}(\infty) = i$ and so, by Theorem 4.1, $f(\mathcal{R})$ is a region whose boundary in $\widehat{\mathbb{C}}$ is the union of the extended real axis with $\{i\}$. But the only region that has this set as a boundary in $\widehat{\mathbb{C}}$ is the upper half-plane with the point i removed (see Figure 4.5). This shows that $f(\mathcal{R}) = \{w : \operatorname{Im} w > 0\} - \{i\}$.

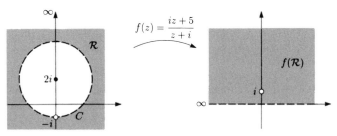

Figure 4.5

To obtain the image under $\widehat{f}$ of the generalized open disc $D = \mathcal{R} \cup \{\infty\}$, we simply attach the image of ∞ to the image of $\mathcal{R}$ to obtain

$$\widehat{f}(D) = \widehat{f}(\mathcal{R} \cup \{\infty\}) = \widehat{f}(\mathcal{R}) \cup \{i\} = \{w : \operatorname{Im} w > 0\}. \quad \blacksquare$$

The image of ∞ fills the hole in the image of $\mathcal{R}$.

This examples illustrates that, far from being a nuisance, a singularity can be used to identify the image set, for the image is the set that contains (or surrounds) the image of the singularity.

Problem 4.3

Let f be the Möbius transformation defined by

$$f(z) = \frac{z - 1}{z - i}.$$

Find the image of the punctured disc $\mathcal{R} = \{z : 0 < |z - i| < 1\}$ under f, and hence find the image of the disc $D = \{z : |z - i| < 1\}$ under $\widehat{f}$.

Use Problem 3.5(c).

4.2 Mappings between generalized open discs

The techniques illustrated in Examples 4.1 and 4.2 can be used to find the image of any generalized open disc. Often, however, we need to be able to reverse this process. That is, given any two generalized open discs we need to be able to find an extended Möbius transformation that maps one of them onto the other.

Example 4.3

Find a Möbius transformation that maps the open disc

$$D = \{z : |z| < 1\}$$

onto the open left half-plane H.

Solution

The boundary of D is the unit circle $C = \{z : |z| = 1\}$ and the boundary in $\widehat{\mathbb{C}}$ of H is the extended imaginary axis. We shall construct a Möbius transformation f whose extension $\widehat{f}$ to $\widehat{\mathbb{C}}$ sends a point that moves around C from 1 to -1 via i, to a point that moves up the imaginary axis from 0 to ∞ via i. Then D is on the left of the point as it moves around C and so the image of D will be on the left of the image point as it moves up the imaginary axis. This will ensure that the image of D is the open left half-plane, as required (see Figure 4.6).

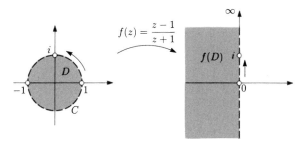

Figure 4.6

A suitable extended Möbius transformation is one that sends 1 to 0, i to i and -1 to ∞. It corresponds to

$$f(z) = i\frac{(z-1)(i+1)}{(z+1)(i-1)} = \frac{z-1}{z+1}. \quad \blacksquare$$

Remarks

1 The Möbius transformation in this example is not unique, since there are many ways of choosing points both on the unit circle and on the imaginary axis. The only constraint is that the points must be selected in the correct order.

2 In this example we constructed a Möbius transformation f by considering properties that the extended function $\widehat{f}$ must have.

We obtained this f by using Formula (2.2) with $\alpha = 1$, $\beta = i$ and $\gamma = -1$, and then multiplying through by i, so that $f(i) = i$.
For example,

$$f(z) = \frac{z-i}{z+i}$$

also works.

Problem 4.4 _____

Find a Möbius transformation that maps the disc $\{z : |z - 2| < 1\}$ onto the open upper half-plane.

The above approach is particularly suitable for constructing a Möbius transformation that sends a generalized open disc onto an open half-plane whose boundary passes through the origin. This is because it is easy to find a transformation that sends points to 0 and ∞. For the same reason, if we wish to find a Möbius transformation that sends a generalized open disc D onto the open unit disc, then it is usually simplest to look for a Möbius transformation that sends inverse points with respect to the boundary of D to the inverse points 0 and ∞ with respect to the unit circle.

Example 4.4

Find a Möbius transformation that maps the open half-plane
$D = \{z : \operatorname{Im} z < \operatorname{Re} z\}$ onto the open unit disc.

Solution

The boundary in $\widehat{\mathbb{C}}$ of D is the extended line with inverse points i and 1. Since $1 \in D$, we can ensure that D maps onto an open disc centred at 0 by mapping 1 to 0 and i to ∞. To ensure that D maps onto the open *unit* disc, we send the point ∞ on the boundary in $\widehat{\mathbb{C}}$ of D to 1 (see Figure 4.7). The extended Möbius transformation that does this is $\widehat{f}$, where $f(z) = \dfrac{z-1}{z-i}$. ∎

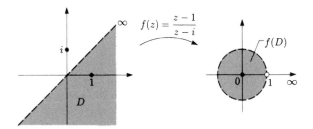

Figure 4.7

Problem 4.5

Find a Möbius transformation that maps the open half-plane
$D = \{z : \operatorname{Re} z < 1\}$ onto the open unit disc.

4.3 Composing conformal mappings (audio-tape)

So far we have examined the effect that Möbius transformations have on generalized open discs. By composing Möbius transformations with some of the other conformal functions that have been introduced in the course we can now consider many other types of region. In this audio-tape subsection, we explore ways of finding the images of various regions under a given composite function. We also explore ways of constructing conformal mappings that send one given region of the complex plane onto another. In the final tape frame we shall need a result which we ask you to prove in the following problem.

Problem 4.6

Show that for $w \in \mathbb{C} - \{-1\}$ and $z \in \mathbb{C} - \{0, -i\}$,

$$ w = \frac{1}{2i}\left(z - \frac{1}{z}\right) \quad \Longleftrightarrow \quad \frac{-w+1}{w+1} = \left(\frac{iz+1}{z+i}\right)^2. $$

(*Hint*: Substitute w from the first equation into the second.)

In the tape frames we express conformal mappings by simply giving the rule relating the variables, for example,

$$ w = \frac{z-1}{z+1} $$

is shorthand for the Möbius transformation $f(z) = \dfrac{z-1}{z+1}$, and even for the corresponding extended Möbius transformation $\widehat{f}$. As you will see, this shorthand is particularly convenient when several such mappings have to be composed.

NOW START THE TAPE.

2. Quadrant $\{z: 0 < \operatorname{Arg} z < \frac{\pi}{2}\}$ onto unit disc

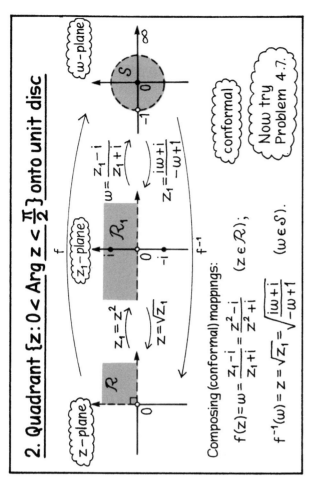

Composing (conformal) mappings:

$$f(z) = \omega = \frac{z_1 - i}{z_1 + i} = \frac{z^2 - i}{z^2 + i} \qquad (z \in \mathcal{R});$$

$$f^{-1}(\omega) = z = \sqrt{z_1} = \sqrt{\frac{i\omega + i}{-\omega + 1}} \qquad (\omega \in \mathcal{S}).$$

Now try Problem 4.7.

3. Semi-disc $\{z: |z| < 1, \operatorname{Im} z > 0\}$ onto upper half-plane

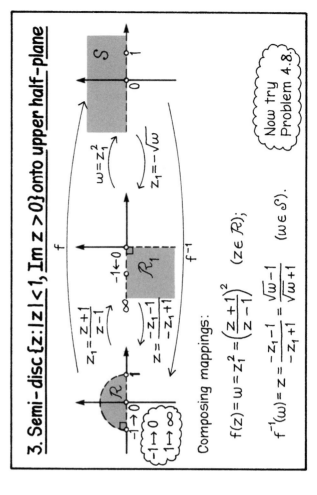

Composing mappings:

$$f(z) = \omega = z_1^2 = \left(\frac{z+1}{z-1}\right)^2 \qquad (z \in \mathcal{R});$$

$$f^{-1}(\omega) = z = \frac{-z_1 - 1}{-z_1 + 1} = \frac{\sqrt{\omega} - 1}{\sqrt{\omega} + 1} \qquad (\omega \in \mathcal{S}).$$

Now try Problem 4.8.

1. Conformal mappings between basic regions

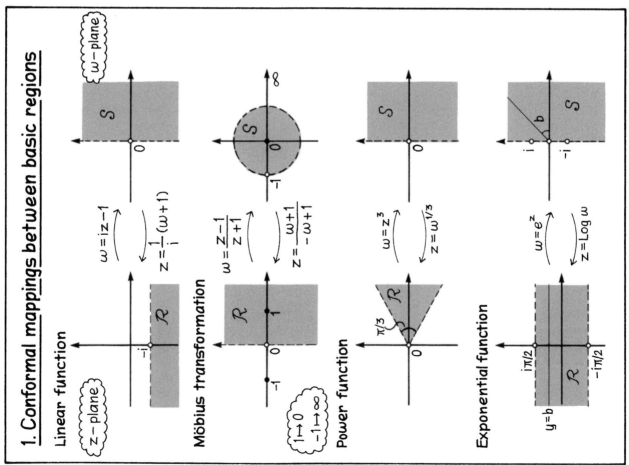

Linear function

Möbius transformation

Power function

Exponential function

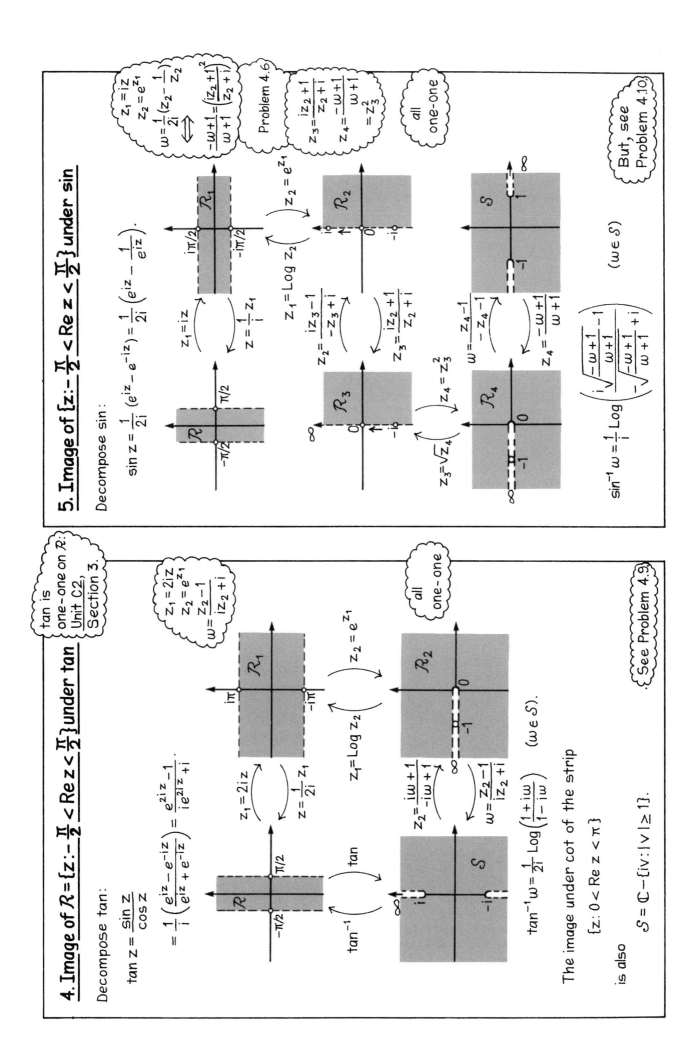

5. Image of $\{z : -\frac{\pi}{2} < \operatorname{Re} z < \frac{\pi}{2}\}$ under sin

Decompose sin:

$$\sin z = \frac{1}{2i}\left(e^{iz} - e^{-iz}\right) = \frac{1}{2i}\left(e^{iz} - \frac{1}{e^{iz}}\right).$$

$$z_1 = iz \qquad z = \frac{1}{i}z_1$$

$$z_2 = e^{z_1} \qquad z_1 = \operatorname{Log} z_2$$

$$z_1 = iz$$
$$z_2 = e^{z_1}$$
$$\omega = \frac{1}{2i}\left(z_2 - \frac{1}{z_2}\right) \quad \Longleftrightarrow \quad \frac{-\omega+1}{\omega+1} = \left(\frac{iz_2+1}{z_2+i}\right)^2$$

Problem 4.6

$$z_2 = \frac{iz_3-1}{-z_3+i} \qquad z_3 = \frac{iz_2+1}{z_2+i}$$

$$\omega = \frac{z_4-1}{-z_4-1} \qquad z_4 = \frac{-\omega+1}{\omega+1}$$

$$z_3 = \frac{iz_2+1}{z_2+i}$$
$$z_4 = \frac{-\omega+1}{\omega+1}$$
$$= z_3^2$$

all one-one

$$z_3 = \sqrt{z_4}$$

$$\sin^{-1}\omega = \frac{1}{i}\operatorname{Log}\left(\frac{i\sqrt{\frac{-\omega+1}{\omega+1}}-1}{-\sqrt{\frac{-\omega+1}{\omega+1}}+i}\right) \qquad (\omega \in \mathcal{S})$$

But, see Problem 4.10

4. Image of $\mathcal{R} = \{z : -\frac{\pi}{2} < \operatorname{Re} z < \frac{\pi}{2}\}$ under tan

Decompose tan:

$$\tan z = \frac{\sin z}{\cos z}$$

$$= \frac{1}{i}\left(\frac{e^{iz}-e^{-iz}}{e^{iz}+e^{-iz}}\right) = \frac{e^{2iz}-1}{ie^{2iz}+i}.$$

$$z_1 = 2iz \qquad z = \frac{1}{2i}z_1$$

$$z_2 = e^{z_1} \qquad z_1 = \operatorname{Log} z_2$$

$$z_1 = 2iz$$
$$z_2 = e^{z_1}$$
$$\omega = \frac{z_2-1}{iz_2+i}$$

tan is one-one on $\mathcal{R}$: Unit C2, Section 3.

$$z_2 = \frac{-i\omega+1}{-i\omega+1} \qquad \omega = \frac{z_2-1}{iz_2+i}$$

all one-one

$$\tan^{-1}\omega = \frac{1}{2i}\operatorname{Log}\left(\frac{1+i\omega}{1-i\omega}\right) \qquad (\omega \in \mathcal{S}).$$

See Problem 4.9.

The image under cot of the strip

$$\{z : 0 < \operatorname{Re} z < \pi\}$$

is also

$$\mathcal{S} = \mathbb{C} - \{iv : |v| \geq 1\}.$$

42

Problem 4.7

(a) Determine a conformal mapping f from the cut plane

$$\mathcal{R} = \mathbb{C} - \{x \in \mathbb{R} : x \leq 0\}$$

onto the open unit disc

$$\mathcal{S} = \{w : |w| < 1\}.$$

(b) Obtain a formula for the inverse function of the restriction of f to $\mathcal{R}$.

Problem 4.8

(a) Determine a conformal mapping f from the 'circular lens'

$$\mathcal{R} = \{z : |z - 1| < \sqrt{2}, |z + 1| < \sqrt{2}\}$$

onto the open right half-plane

$$\mathcal{S} = \{w : \operatorname{Re} w > 0\}.$$

(*Hint:* What is the angle of the boundary of $\mathcal{R}$ at i?)

(b) Obtain a formula for the inverse function of the restriction of f to $\mathcal{R}$.

Problem 4.9

(a) Prove the identity

$$\cot z = \tan(\pi/2 - z).$$

(b) Determine the image under the function cot of the strip

$$\mathcal{R} = \{z : 0 < \operatorname{Re} z < \pi\}.$$

(c) Obtain a formula for the inverse function of the restriction of cot to $\mathcal{R}$.

4.4 The Joukowski function

In this subsection we construct a conformal mapping from the region surrounding the closed unit disc to the region surrounding the interval $[-2, 2]$, by using the composition of conformal mappings illustrated in Figure 4.8. This mapping has an important role to play in *Unit D2*.

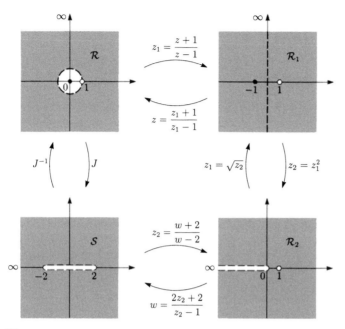

Figure 4.8

The region $\mathcal{R} = \{z : |z| > 1\}$ in the top left-hand corner has a boundary in $\widehat{\mathbb{C}}$ that consists of the unit circle together with the point at infinity. The unit circle has inverse points 0 and ∞, which the extended Möbius transformation given by $z_1 = (z + 1)/(z - 1)$ sends to the points -1 and 1, respectively. Also, the point 1 on the unit circle is sent to ∞, so the unit circle must map onto the extended imaginary axis. The boundary point of $\mathcal{R}$ at ∞ maps to 1, and so by Theorem 4.1, the region $\mathcal{R}$ is mapped onto the right half-plane with the point 1 removed. We call this image $\mathcal{R}_1 = \{z : \operatorname{Re} z > 0\} - \{1\}$.

Next we apply the square function to send $\mathcal{R}_1$, the right half-plane with the point 1 removed, onto the standard cut plane with the point 1 removed, which we denote by $\mathcal{R}_2 = (\mathbb{C} - \{x \in \mathbb{R} : x \leq 0\}) - \{1\}$.

Finally the extended Möbius transformation given by $w = (2z_2 + 2)/(z_2 - 1)$ maps the 'missing' point at 1 to ∞, and it sends the points 0 and ∞ to the points -2 and 2, respectively. It follows that the negative real axis together with 0 and ∞ is mapped onto the interval $[-2, 2]$. By Theorem 4.1, the standard cut plane with the point 1 removed is mapped onto the region $\mathcal{S} = \mathbb{C} - [-2, 2]$ surrounding the interval $[-2, 2]$, as required.

Overall, the mapping from $\mathcal{R}$ onto $\mathcal{S}$ is given by

$$w = \frac{2z_2 + 2}{z_2 - 1} = \frac{2z_1^2 + 2}{z_1^2 - 1} = \frac{2\left(\dfrac{z+1}{z-1}\right)^2 + 2}{\left(\dfrac{z+1}{z-1}\right)^2 - 1}.$$

On simplifying this, we obtain

$$w = \frac{2(z+1)^2 + 2(z-1)^2}{(z+1)^2 - (z-1)^2} = \frac{2\left(z^2 + 2z + 1\right) + 2\left(z^2 - 2z + 1\right)}{\left(z^2 + 2z + 1\right) - \left(z^2 - 2z + 1\right)}$$

$$= \frac{\left(4z^2 + 4\right)}{4z} = z + \frac{1}{z}.$$

The function from $\mathcal{R}$ onto $\mathcal{S}$ defined by this rule is usually denoted by J. Thus

$$J(z) = z + \frac{1}{z} \qquad (z \in \mathcal{R}).$$

(In fact, this function is the restriction to $\mathcal{R}$ of the **Joukowski function**

$$J(z) = z + \frac{1}{z} \qquad (z \in \mathbb{C} - \{0\}),$$

The Russian Nikolai Egerovich Joukowski (1847–1921) was one of the first to make use of analytic function theory in aerodynamics.

which we will use in *Unit D2*.) Since all the mappings in Figure 4.8 from which J is composed are one-one and analytic on the regions on which they act, it follows that J is one-one and analytic on $\mathcal{R}$. The inverse of the Joukowski function maps $\mathcal{S}$ onto $\mathcal{R}$ and can be obtained from the inverses of the constituent mappings shown in Figure 4.8, as follows:

$$J^{-1}(w) = z = \frac{z_1 + 1}{z_1 - 1} = \frac{\sqrt{z_2} + 1}{\sqrt{z_2} - 1} = \frac{\sqrt{\dfrac{w+2}{w-2}} + 1}{\sqrt{\dfrac{w+2}{w-2}} - 1}. \qquad (4.1)$$

This expression is more difficult to simplify than the expression for J because of the principal square roots. However, by initially restricting our attention to real values of w in $\{x \in \mathbb{R} : x > 2\}$, we can argue as follows:

Note that if you try to solve
$$w = J(z) = z + 1/z$$
directly to obtain z in terms of w, then the resulting formula
$$z = \tfrac{1}{2}(w \pm \sqrt{w^2 - 4})$$
does not tell you which square root to use.

$$
\begin{aligned}
J^{-1}(w) &= \frac{\sqrt{w+2} + \sqrt{w-2}}{\sqrt{w+2} - \sqrt{w-2}} \\
&= \left(\frac{\sqrt{w+2} + \sqrt{w-2}}{\sqrt{w+2} - \sqrt{w-2}} \right) \left(\frac{\sqrt{w+2} + \sqrt{w-2}}{\sqrt{w+2} + \sqrt{w-2}} \right) \\
&= \frac{(w+2) + 2\sqrt{(w-2)(w+2)} + (w-2)}{(w+2) - (w-2)} \\
&= \tfrac{1}{2}\left(w + \sqrt{w^2 - 4} \right) \\
&= \tfrac{1}{2}\left(w + w\sqrt{1 - 4/w^2} \right).
\end{aligned}
$$

The identity
$$\sqrt{w-2}\sqrt{w+2} = \sqrt{w^2 - 4}$$
is evident if w is real and greater than 2. It is false in general: for example, try $w = -2i$.

But this last expression is actually defined throughout $\mathcal{S}$. Indeed, if $w \in \mathcal{S}$, then Figure 4.9 shows that

$$1 - \frac{4}{w^2} = \frac{w_1 - 4}{w_1}, \qquad \text{where } w_1 = w^2,$$

belongs to the domain of the principal square root function.

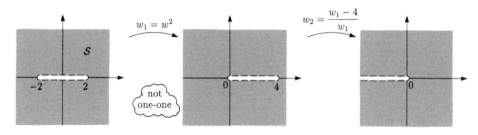

Figure 4.9

Since the rule for $J^{-1}(w)$ in Equation (4.1) and the rule $\tfrac{1}{2}\left(w + w\sqrt{1 - 4/w^2} \right)$ both define analytic functions on $\mathcal{S}$ and agree on $\{x \in \mathbb{R} : x > 2\}$, it follows from the Uniqueness Theorem that they also agree on $\mathcal{S}$. So

Unit B3, Theorem 5.5

$$J^{-1}(w) = \tfrac{1}{2}(w + w\sqrt{1 - 4/w^2}) \qquad (w \in \mathcal{S}).$$

This formula for J^{-1} will be needed in *Unit D2*.

The following problem, which is quite challenging, asks you to use a similar method to find the simpler expression for the inverse sine function, given in *Unit B3*, Section 4.

Problem 4.10 _____

(a) Use the formula for the inverse sine function, given in Frame 5 of the audio tape, to show that if $w \in \{x \in \mathbb{R} : |x| < 1\}$ then

$$\sin^{-1} w = \frac{1}{i} \operatorname{Log}\left(iw + \sqrt{1 - w^2}\right).$$

(b) Show that if $w \in \mathcal{S}$, where $\mathcal{S} = \mathbb{C} - \{x \in \mathbb{R} : |x| \geq 1\}$, then both $1 - w^2$ and $iw + \sqrt{1 - w^2}$ lie in the standard cut plane

$$\mathbb{C} - \{x \in \mathbb{R} : x \leq 0\}.$$

(*Hint*: Assume that $iw + \sqrt{1 - w^2} = -a$ for some $a \geq 0$ and show that this leads to a contradiction.)

(c) Use your results to parts (a) and (b) to show that

$$\sin^{-1} w = \frac{1}{i} \operatorname{Log}\left(iw + \sqrt{1 - w^2}\right), \qquad \text{for } w \in \mathcal{S}.$$

(d) Use the Inverse Function Rule to show that   *Unit C2*, Theorem 3.3

$$\left(\sin^{-1}\right)'(w) = \frac{1}{\sqrt{1 - w^2}},$$

for all $w \in \{x \in \mathbb{R} : |x| < 1\}$, and hence for all $w \in \mathcal{S}$.

---

5 THE RIEMANN MAPPING THEOREM

After working through this section, you should be able to: This section is intended for reading only.

(a) appreciate the role of the Riemann Mapping Theorem in complex analysis.

In Section 4 you saw how to construct one-one conformal mappings between many pairs of regions. For example, the function

$$f(z) = \frac{\sqrt{z} - 1}{\sqrt{z} + 1} \qquad (z \in \mathbb{C} - \{x \in \mathbb{R} : x \leq 0\})$$ Problem 4.7

is a one-one conformal mapping from the cut plane $\mathbb{C} - \{x \in \mathbb{R} : x \leq 0\}$ onto the open unit disc $\{w : |w| < 1\}$ (see Figure 5.1).

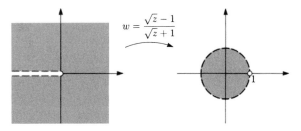

Figure 5.1

All the conformal mappings constructed in Section 4 were given by explicit formulas involving elementary analytic functions. In this section, we consider a more general problem, posed by Riemann.

> For which pairs of simply-connected regions $\mathcal{R}_1$ and $\mathcal{R}_2$, is there a one-one conformal mapping from $\mathcal{R}_1$ onto $\mathcal{R}_2$?

Recall that a region is simply-connected if it has no 'holes' in it (*Unit B2*, Section 1).

It is easy to find a pair of simply-connected regions for which such a mapping does not exist. For example, if $\mathcal{R}_1 = \mathbb{C}$ and $\mathcal{R}_2 = \{w : |w| < 1\}$, then there is no one-one conformal mapping from $\mathcal{R}_1$ onto $\mathcal{R}_2$. Indeed, any such mapping f would be a bounded entire function and hence would have to be constant by Liouville's Theorem.   *Unit B2*, Theorem 2.2

In view of this example, it is perhaps surprising that Riemann, in 1851, came to the following conclusion:

if $\mathcal{R}_1$ and $\mathcal{R}_2$ are *any* two simply-connected regions, neither equal to $\mathbb{C}$, then there is a one-one conformal mapping from $\mathcal{R}_1$ onto $\mathcal{R}_2$.

Since such simply-connected regions may be complicated (see, for example, Figure 5.2), we should not expect to be able to construct such a mapping explicitly. However, Riemann claimed only the *existence* of such a mapping, without specifying how to calculate it. The following special case of this result, in which one of the regions is the open unit disc, is known as the Riemann Mapping Theorem.

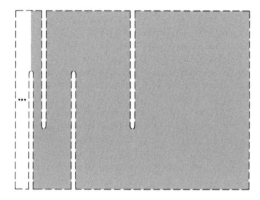

Figure 5.2   A simply-connected region

Theorem 5.1 Riemann Mapping Theorem

Let $\mathcal{R}$ be a simply-connected region, not equal to $\mathbb{C}$, and let D be the open unit disc. Then there is a one-one conformal mapping from $\mathcal{R}$ onto D.

Remark   In fact, if $\alpha \in \mathcal{R}$, then it can be shown that there is a unique one-one conformal mapping from $\mathcal{R}$ onto D such that

$$f(\alpha) = 0 \quad \text{and} \quad f'(\alpha) > 0.$$

See Exercise 4.5(b) for an important special case of this result.

Theorem 5.1 leads to a complete solution to Riemann's problem, as follows. If $\mathcal{R}_1$, $\mathcal{R}_2$ is any pair of simply-connected regions, neither of which equals $\mathbb{C}$, then Theorem 5.1 implies the existence of one-one conformal mappings f_1, f_2, from $\mathcal{R}_1$, $\mathcal{R}_2$ respectively, onto D (see Figure 5.3). Then f_2^{-1} is a one-one conformal mapping from D onto $\mathcal{R}_2$, and hence the composite function $f = f_2^{-1} \circ f_1$ is a one-one conformal mapping from $\mathcal{R}_1$ onto $\mathcal{R}_2$.

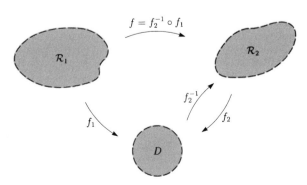

Figure 5.3

In fact, Riemann did not supply a full proof of Theorem 5.1 and his argument can be made to work only for regions with fairly well-behaved boundaries (better than in Figure 5.2). A full proof of Theorem 5.1 was not given until about 1910 (by Hilbert, Osgood, and Koebe, independently). It would take too long to supply all the details of a proof here, but one method is to construct a sequence of functions $\{f_n\}$ which map $\mathcal{R}$ one-one and conformally onto regions which approximate to D more and more closely as $n \to \infty$, and then show that the limit function $f = \lim\limits_{n \to \infty} f_n$ maps $\mathcal{R}$ one-one and conformally onto D.

As is often the case in mathematics, the Riemann Mapping Theorem answers one question, but poses many more! For example, it is natural to expect that the conformal mapping f will lead to some correspondence between the boundary of the simply-connected region $\mathcal{R}$ and the boundary of the unit disc D, and to try and discover the nature of this correspondence. (You may like to try and imagine how the boundary of the region in Figure 5.2 would correspond to the boundary of the open unit disc.)

Another related question concerns those functions f which are defined by power series of the form

$$f(z) = z + a_2 z^2 + a_3 z^3 + \cdots \qquad (|z| < 1),$$

and which are one-one on $D = \{z : |z| < 1\}$. In 1916, L. Bieberbach proved that for such a function f we must have $|a_2| \leq 2$ and he conjectured that

$$|a_n| \leq n, \qquad \text{for all } n \geq 2.$$

Over the years, this **Bieberbach conjecture** was established for $n = 3, 4, 5$ and 6 and finally in 1984 it was proved for all $n \geq 2$, by L. de Branges. Notice that the above inequalities are certainly 'best possible' because equality is achieved for the function

$$
\begin{aligned}
f(z) &= z + 2z^2 + 3z^3 + \cdots \\
&= \frac{z}{(1-z)^2} \\
&= \tfrac{1}{4}\left(\frac{1+z}{1-z}\right)^2 - \tfrac{1}{4},
\end{aligned}
$$

This function f is known as Koebe's function.

which is analytic on D and maps D one-one onto the simply-connected region $\mathbb{C} - \{u \in \mathbb{R} : u \leq -\tfrac{1}{4}\}$.

The function
$$z \longmapsto \left(\frac{1+z}{1-z}\right)^2$$
maps D onto the standard cut plane; see Problem 4.7(b).

EXERCISES

Section 1

Exercise 1.1

(a) Find a linear function which maps the half-plane $\{z : \operatorname{Im} z > 1\}$ onto the half-plane $\{z : \operatorname{Re} z > 2\}$.

(b) Find a linear function which maps the disc $\{z : |z - i| < 1\}$ onto the disc $\{z : |z| < 10\}$.

Exercise 1.2

(a) For each of the following lines and circles, decide whether the image under the reciprocal function is a line or a circle, and whether or not it passes through the origin.

(i) $2x - y = 0$ (ii) $x^2 + y^2 = 2$

(iii) $x^2 + (y - 2)^2 = 4$ (iv) $2x + y = 1$

(b) Find an equation for the image set for (i) and (ii) of part (a).

Exercise 1.3 Determine the extended function $\widehat{f}$ associated with each of the following functions f.

(a) $f(z) = 2z + 6$ (b) $f(z) = \dfrac{1}{z-1}$

Section 2

Exercise 2.1 Let

$$f(z) = \frac{z-i}{1+iz}, \quad g(z) = \frac{z-1}{z+2i}, \quad h(z) = \frac{z}{2z-i}.$$

(a) Which of the functions f, g and h are Möbius transformations?

(b) For each of the Möbius transformations you identified in part (a), write down its associated extended Möbius transformation and its inverse function.

Exercise 2.2 Find the composition $\widehat{g} \circ \widehat{f}$, where f and g are the Möbius transformations

$$f(z) = \frac{z+1}{z-1}, \quad g(z) = \frac{z-2}{z+i}.$$

Exercise 2.3 For each of the following triples, find the extended Möbius transformation which sends the three points to the standard triple 0, 1, ∞, respectively.

(a) $1, -1, \infty$ (b) $1, 0, -1$ (c) $1+i, 2-i, 0$

Exercise 2.4 Find the extended Möbius transformation which sends $2i$ to 1, $1 + 2i$ to $1 + i$ and 1 to i.

Section 3

Exercise 3.1 Use the three-point trick to find the image of the circle $C = \{z : |z| = 2\}$ under each of the extended Möbius transformations $\widehat{f}$, where

(a) $f(z) = \dfrac{z+2i}{z-2}$;   (b) $f(z) = \dfrac{z-2}{z}$.

Exercise 3.2 For each of the following generalized circles C, find the image of C under the extended Möbius transformation $\widehat{f}$, where

$$f(z) = \frac{z-i}{z+i}.$$

(a) $C = \{z : |z+i| = 1\}$ (b) $C = \{z : |z-i| = 1\}$

Give your answers in Apollonian form, where appropriate, and state whether the images are circles or extended lines.

Exercise 3.3 Find the centre and radius of each of the following circles.

(a) $\{z : |z-i| = 2|z+3i|\}$ (b) $\{z : |z| = 6|z+i|\}$

Exercise 3.4

(a) Determine the point α such that α and $\beta = 1+i$ are inverse points with respect to each of the following circles.

    (i) $C_1 = \{z : |z| = 2\}$ (ii) $C_2 = \{z : |z-i| = \frac{1}{2}\}$

(b) Write down the equations of the two circles in part (a) in Apollonian form.

Exercise 3.5 Determine the point α such that α and $\beta = 2 - i$ are inverse points with respect to each of the following extended lines. Hence write down an equation for each of the extended lines in Apollonian form.

(a) the extended real axis   (b) $\{z : \operatorname{Re} z + \operatorname{Im} z = 0\} \cup \{\infty\}$

Section 4

Exercise 4.1 Write down the boundary in $\widehat{\mathbb{C}}$ of each of the following subsets of $\widehat{\mathbb{C}}$.

(a) $\{z : |z - i| < 2\}$ (b) $\{z : \operatorname{Im} z < -1\}$

(c) $\{z : |z + i| > 1\} \cup \{\infty\}$ (d) $\{z : |z + i| > 1\}$

Exercise 4.2

(a) Find the image of the open disc $\{z : |z - 1| < 2\}$ under the Möbius transformation

$$f(z) = \frac{z + i}{z + 1}.$$

(b) Find the image of the punctured open disc $\{z : 0 < |z + i| < 1\}$ under the Möbius transformation

$$f(z) = \frac{z - i}{z + i},$$

and hence find the image of the open disc $\{z : |z + i| < 1\}$ under the extended Möbius transformation $\widehat{f}$.

Exercise 4.3 Find a Möbius transformation which maps the open half-plane $\{z : \operatorname{Im} z + \operatorname{Re} z < 1\}$ onto the open disc $\{z : |z| < 2\}$.

Exercise 4.4 Determine a one-one conformal function from the crescent-shaped region

$$\mathcal{R} = \{z : |z - 1| > 1, |z - 2| < 2\}$$

onto the open right half-plane.

(*Hint:* First consider the effect on $\mathcal{R}$ of the reciprocal function.)

Exercise 4.5

(a) Show that every Möbius transformation f which maps the open unit disc onto itself is of the form

$$f(z) = e^{i\theta} \left(\frac{z - \alpha}{\overline{\alpha}z - 1} \right),$$

where $|\alpha| < 1$ and $\theta \in \mathbb{R}$.

(b) Deduce from part (a) that there is only one Möbius transformation f which maps the open unit disc onto itself and satisfies

$$f(0) = 0 \quad \text{and} \quad f'(0) > 0.$$

SOLUTIONS TO THE PROBLEMS

Section 1

1.1

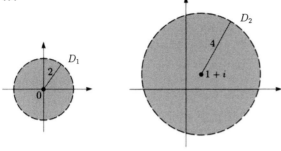

We can map D_1 onto D_2 in two stages. We first scale by the factor 2 and then translate by $1 + i$; no rotation is needed. Overall this can be achieved by the linear function

$$f(z) = 2z + (1 + i).$$

1.2

In $y + 4x = 1$, we replace x by $u/(u^2 + v^2)$ and y by $-v/(u^2 + v^2)$ to obtain

$$\left(\frac{-v}{u^2 + v^2}\right) + 4\left(\frac{u}{u^2 + v^2}\right) = 1.$$

By multiplying throughout by $u^2 + v^2$, we obtain

$$u^2 + v^2 - 4u + v = 0.$$

If we complete the squares, then this equation becomes

$$(u - 2)^2 + (v + \tfrac{1}{2})^2 = 4\tfrac{1}{4}.$$

(The image is the circle with radius $\frac{1}{2}\sqrt{17}$ and centre $2 - \frac{1}{2}i$, except for 0.)

1.3

In $y = x$, we replace x by $u/(u^2 + v^2)$ and y by $-v/(u^2 + v^2)$ to obtain

$$\frac{-v}{u^2 + v^2} = \frac{u}{u^2 + v^2},$$

that is, $v = -u \; (u^2 + v^2 \neq 0)$.

(The image is the reflection of the given line in the real axis.)

1.4

(a) On replacing x by $u/(u^2 + v^2)$ and y by $-v/(u^2 + v^2)$ in $x^2 + y^2 = 4$, we obtain

$$\left(\frac{u}{u^2 + v^2}\right)^2 + \left(\frac{-v}{u^2 + v^2}\right)^2 = 4.$$

Thus

$$\frac{1}{u^2 + v^2} = 4,$$

and so

$$u^2 + v^2 = \tfrac{1}{4}.$$

(This is the equation of the circle of radius $\frac{1}{2}$ centred at the origin.)

(b) The equation $(x - 3)^2 + (y - 4)^2 = 25$, can be rewritten as

$$x^2 + y^2 - 6x - 8y = 0.$$

On replacing x by $u/(u^2 + v^2)$ and y by $-v/(u^2 + v^2)$, we obtain

$$\left(\frac{u}{u^2 + v^2}\right)^2 + \left(\frac{-v}{u^2 + v^2}\right)^2 - 6\left(\frac{u}{u^2 + v^2}\right) - 8\left(\frac{-v}{u^2 + v^2}\right) = 0.$$

As usual, the first two terms combine to give $\dfrac{1}{u^2 + v^2}$, and so the equation becomes

$$\left(\frac{1}{u^2 + v^2}\right) - 6\left(\frac{u}{u^2 + v^2}\right) - 8\left(\frac{-v}{u^2 + v^2}\right) = 0.$$

By multiplying through by $u^2 + v^2 (\neq 0)$ and rearranging, we obtain

$$6u - 8v = 1.$$

(Thus the image is the line $6u - 8v = 1$.)

1.5

(a) The line or circle has equation

$$a\left(x^2 + y^2\right) + bx + cy + d = 0,$$

where $a, b, c, d \in \mathbb{R}$ and $b^2 + c^2 > 4ad$.

On replacing x by $u/(u^2 + v^2)$ and y by $-v/(u^2 + v^2)$, we obtain

$$a\left(\left(\frac{u}{u^2 + v^2}\right)^2 + \left(\frac{-v}{u^2 + v^2}\right)^2\right)$$
$$+ b\left(\frac{u}{u^2 + v^2}\right) + c\left(\frac{-v}{u^2 + v^2}\right) + d = 0,$$

that is,

$$a\left(\frac{1}{u^2 + v^2}\right) + b\left(\frac{u}{u^2 + v^2}\right) + c\left(\frac{-v}{u^2 + v^2}\right) + d = 0.$$

By multiplying through by $u^2 + v^2 (\neq 0)$ and interchanging the first and last term on the left of the equation, we obtain

$$d\left(u^2 + v^2\right) + bu - cv + a = 0, \quad \text{where } b^2 + (-c)^2 > 4da.$$

(We have used $(-c)^2 = c^2$ and $ad = da$ to rewrite the original condition $b^2 + c^2 > 4ad$.)

The argument in the other direction is the same as that above, but x, y, a, b, c, d are interchanged with $u, v, d, b, -c, a$, respectively.

(b) The various cases arise as follows:

(i) $a = d = 0$;

(ii) $a = 0$, $d \neq 0$;

(iii) $a \neq 0$, $d = 0$;

(iv) $a \neq 0$, $d \neq 0$.

1.6

(a) This is a line that does not pass through the origin, so its image is a circle through the origin.

(b) This is a circle through the origin, so its image is a line which does not pass through the origin.

(c) This is a circle that does not pass through the origin, so its image is a circle which does not pass through the origin.

(d) This is a line through the origin, so its image is a line through the origin.

1.7

(a) Here $f(z) \to \infty$ as $z \to -\frac{1}{3}$, so $\widehat{f}\left(-\frac{1}{3}\right) = \infty$. Also

$$\lim_{w \to 0} f(1/w) = \lim_{w \to 0} \frac{(6/w) + 4}{(3/w) + 1} = \lim_{w \to 0} \frac{6 + 4w}{3 + w} = 2,$$

and so f has a removable singularity at ∞, with $\widehat{f}(\infty) = 2$. Thus

$$\widehat{f}(z) = \begin{cases} f(z), & z \in \mathbb{C} - \left\{-\frac{1}{3}\right\}, \\ \infty, & z = -\frac{1}{3}, \\ 2, & z = \infty. \end{cases}$$

(b) Here $f(z) \to \infty$ as $z \to 0$, so $\widehat{f}(0) = \infty$. Also

$$\lim_{w \to 0} f(1/w) = \lim_{w \to 0} w = 0,$$

and so f has a removable singularity at ∞, with $\widehat{f}(\infty) = 0$. Thus

$$\widehat{f}(z) = \begin{cases} f(z), & z \in \mathbb{C} - \{0\}, \\ \infty, & z = 0, \\ 0, & z = \infty. \end{cases}$$

(c) Here $f(1/w) \to \infty$ as $w \to 0$, and so f has a pole at ∞. Thus

$$\widehat{f}(z) = \begin{cases} f(z), & z \in \mathbb{C}, \\ \infty, & z = \infty. \end{cases}$$

(d) Here $f(z) \to \infty$ as $z \to -\frac{1}{2}$, so $\widehat{f}\left(-\frac{1}{2}\right) = \infty$. Also

$$\lim_{w \to 0} f(1/w) = \lim_{w \to 0} \frac{1}{(2/w) + 1} = \lim_{w \to 0} \frac{w}{2 + w} = 0$$

and so f has a removable singularity at ∞, with $\widehat{f}(\infty) = 0$. Thus

$$\widehat{f}(z) = \begin{cases} f(z) & z \in \mathbb{C} - \{-\frac{1}{2}\}, \\ \infty, & z = -\frac{1}{2}, \\ 0, & z = \infty. \end{cases}$$

(e) Since $f(z) = z + \dfrac{1}{z}$, for $z \in \mathbb{C} - \{0\}$,

$$f(z) \to \infty \text{ as } z \to 0,$$

so $\widehat{f}(0) = \infty$. Also

$$f(1/w) = \frac{(1/w)^2 + 1}{1/w}$$
$$= (1/w) + w \to \infty, \text{ as } w \to 0,$$

and so f has a pole at ∞. Thus

$$\widehat{f}(z) = \begin{cases} f(z), & z \in \mathbb{C} - \{0\}, \\ \infty, & z = 0, \\ \infty, & z = \infty. \end{cases}$$

Section 2

2.1 **(a)** Möbius: $a = d = 0$, $b = 3$, $c = 1$; $ad - bc = -3 \neq 0$.

(b) Möbius: $a = 2$, $b = 3i$, $c = 1$, $d = 0$; $ad - bc = -3i \neq 0$.

(c) Not Möbius: $f(z) = \left(z^2 + 3\right)/z$ is not of the correct form.

(d) Not Möbius: $ad - bc = 0$.

(e) Not Möbius: $ad - bc = 1 \times (-1) - i \times i = 0$.

(f) Möbius: $a = 1$, $b = 1 - i$, $c = 3$, $d = 2$; $ad - bc = -1 + 3i \neq 0$.

2.2 **(a)** $\widehat{f}(z) = \begin{cases} f(z), & z \in \mathbb{C} - \{\frac{1}{3}\}, \\ \infty, & z = \frac{1}{3}, \\ -\frac{2}{3}, & z = \infty. \end{cases}$

(b) $\widehat{f}(z) = \begin{cases} f(z), & z \in \mathbb{C} - \{-\frac{2}{3}\}, \\ \infty, & z = -\frac{2}{3}, \\ \frac{1}{3}, & z = \infty. \end{cases}$

(c) $\widehat{f}(z) = \begin{cases} f(z), & z \in \mathbb{C}, \\ \infty, & z = \infty. \end{cases}$

2.3 **(a)** By Theorem 2.2, the extended Möbius transformation $\widehat{f}$ is a one-one function from $\widehat{\mathbb{C}}$ onto $\widehat{\mathbb{C}}$. Also $\widehat{f}\left(-\frac{2}{3}\right) = \infty$ and $\widehat{f}(\infty) = \frac{1}{3}$. So f is a one-one function from $\mathbb{C} - \left\{-\frac{2}{3}\right\}$ onto $\mathbb{C} - \left\{\frac{1}{3}\right\}$. Thus, for each $w \in \mathbb{C} - \left\{\frac{1}{3}\right\}$, we have

$$w = \frac{z - i}{3z + 2} \iff 3zw + 2w = z - i$$
$$\iff 3zw - z = -2w - i$$
$$\iff z = \frac{2w + i}{-3w + 1}.$$

The inverse function of f is therefore the Möbius transformation

$$f^{-1}(w) = \frac{2w + i}{-3w + 1} \quad (w \in \mathbb{C} - \left\{\tfrac{1}{3}\right\}).$$

Since $\widehat{f}(\infty) = \frac{1}{3}$ and $\widehat{f}\left(-\frac{2}{3}\right) = \infty$, we have

$$\widehat{f}^{-1}\left(\tfrac{1}{3}\right) = \infty \quad \text{and} \quad \widehat{f}^{-1}(\infty) = -\tfrac{2}{3}.$$

But $\widehat{f^{-1}}\left(\frac{1}{3}\right) = \infty$ and $\widehat{f^{-1}}(\infty) = -\frac{2}{3}$, so that $\widehat{f}^{-1} = \widehat{f^{-1}}$, as required.

(b) By Theorem 2.2, the extended Möbius transformation $\widehat{f}$ is a one-one function from $\widehat{\mathbb{C}}$ onto $\widehat{\mathbb{C}}$. Also $\widehat{f}\left(\frac{4}{3}\right) = \infty$ and $\widehat{f}(\infty) = \frac{1}{3}$. So f is a one-one function from $\mathbb{C} - \left\{\frac{4}{3}\right\}$ onto $\mathbb{C} - \left\{\frac{1}{3}\right\}$. Thus, for each $w \in \mathbb{C} - \left\{\frac{1}{3}\right\}$, we have

$$w = \frac{z + 2i}{3z - 4} \iff 3zw - 4w = z + 2i$$
$$\iff 3zw - z = 4w + 2i$$
$$\iff z = \frac{4w + 2i}{3w - 1}.$$

The inverse function of f is therefore the Möbius transformation

$$f^{-1}(w) = \frac{4w + 2i}{3w - 1} \quad (w \in \mathbb{C} - \left\{\tfrac{1}{3}\right\}).$$

Since $\widehat{f}(\infty) = \frac{1}{3}$ and $\widehat{f}\left(\frac{4}{3}\right) = \infty$, we have

$$\widehat{f}^{-1}\left(\tfrac{1}{3}\right) = \infty \quad \text{and} \quad \widehat{f}^{-1}(\infty) = \tfrac{4}{3}.$$

But $\widehat{f^{-1}}\left(\frac{1}{3}\right) = \infty$ and $\widehat{f^{-1}}(\infty) = \frac{4}{3}$, so that $\widehat{f}^{-1} = \widehat{f^{-1}}$, as required.

2.4 Let f be the Möbius transformation in Theorem 2.3. Then, by Theorem 2.2, $\widehat{f}$ is a one-one function from $\widehat{\mathbb{C}}$ onto $\widehat{\mathbb{C}}$. Also $\widehat{f}(\infty) = a/c$ and $\widehat{f}(-d/c) = \infty$. So f is a one-one function from $\mathbb{C} - \{-d/c\}$ onto $\mathbb{C} - \{a/c\}$. Thus, for each $w \in \mathbb{C} - \{a/c\}$, we have

$$w = \frac{az + b}{cz + d} \iff czw + dw = az + b$$
$$\iff czw - az = -dw + b$$
$$\iff z = \frac{-dw + b}{cw - a}$$
$$\iff z = \frac{dw - b}{-cw + a}.$$

The inverse function of f is therefore the Möbius transformation

$$f^{-1}(w) = \frac{dw - b}{-cw + a} \quad (w \in \mathbb{C} - \{a/c\}),$$

as required. Since $\widehat{f}(\infty) = a/c$ and $\widehat{f}(-d/c) = \infty$, we have

$$\widehat{f}^{-1}(a/c) = \infty \quad \text{and} \quad \widehat{f}^{-1}(\infty) = -d/c.$$

But $\widehat{f^{-1}}(a/c) = \infty$ and $\widehat{f^{-1}}(\infty) = -d/c$, so that $\widehat{f}^{-1} = \widehat{f^{-1}}$, as required.

2.5 Theorem 2.3 states that we can write down the inverse function of a Möbius transformation $f(z) = (az + b)/(cz + d)$ by interchanging the coefficients a, d and reversing the signs of the coefficients b, c.

By applying this rule to the Möbius transformations in Problem 2.3, we obtain

(a) $f^{-1}(z) = \dfrac{2z + i}{-3z + 1}$ ($z \in \mathbb{C} - \{1/3\}$);

(b) $f^{-1}(z) = \dfrac{-4z - 2i}{-3z + 1} = \dfrac{4z + 2i}{3z - 1}$ ($z \in \mathbb{C} - \{1/3\}$).

In each case, $\widehat{f}^{-1} = \widehat{f^{-1}}$ follows from Theorem 2.3.

2.6 For z in the domain of $g \circ f$, we have

$$(\widehat{g} \circ \widehat{f})(z) = g\left(\frac{z + i}{z - i}\right) = \frac{\left(\dfrac{z + i}{z - i}\right) + 2}{\left(\dfrac{z + i}{z - i}\right) - 2}$$

$$= \frac{(z + i) + 2(z - i)}{(z + i) - 2(z - i)}$$

$$= \frac{3z - i}{-z + 3i}.$$

So, by Theorem 2.4, $\widehat{g} \circ \widehat{f}$ is the extended Möbius transformation $\widehat{h}$, where

$$h(z) = \frac{3z - i}{-z + 3i}.$$

2.7 (a) The fixed points of the extended Möbius transformation $\widehat{f}$ are ∞, and the solution of $\frac{1}{2}z + 1 = z$, which is 2.

(b) The fixed points of the extended Möbius transformation $\widehat{f}$ are the solutions (in $\mathbb{C}$) of $1/z = z$, which are 1 and -1.

2.8 In each case, we use Formula (2.2).

(a) Here the transformation is $\widehat{f}$, where

$$f(z) = \frac{(z - 2)}{(z + 2)}\frac{(2i + 2)}{(2i - 2)} = \frac{(z - 2)}{(z + 2)}(-i) = \frac{-iz + 2i}{z + 2}.$$

(b) Here the transformation is $\widehat{f}$, where

$$f(z) = \frac{(z - i)}{(z - 1)}\frac{(\infty - 1)}{(\infty - i)} = \frac{z - i}{z - 1}.$$

(c) Here the transformation is $\widehat{f}$, where

$$f(z) = \frac{(z - \infty)}{(z - 1)}\frac{(3i - 1)}{(3i - \infty)} = \frac{3i - 1}{z - 1}.$$

(d) Here the transformation is $\widehat{f}$, where

$$f(z) = \frac{(z - (1 + i))}{(z - \infty)}\frac{(0 - \infty)}{(0 - (1 + i))}$$

$$= \frac{z - (1 + i)}{-(1 + i)}$$

$$= -\tfrac{1}{2}(1 - i)z + 1.$$

2.9 We find the required transformation by using the Implicit Formula, which in this case is

$$\frac{(z - 2)(2i + 2)}{(z + 2)(2i - 2)} = \frac{(w - i)(\infty - 1)}{(w - 1)(\infty - i)} = \frac{w - i}{w - 1}.$$

By evaluating the constant term and cross-multiplying, we obtain

$$(z - 2)(w - 1)(-i) = (w - i)(z + 2),$$

that is,

$$-zwi + zi + 2wi - 2i = wz + 2w - iz - 2i.$$

On collecting the w terms on the left, we obtain

$$w(-zi - z) + w(2i - 2) = -2iz,$$

and so

$$w = \frac{-2iz}{z(-1 - i) + 2(i - 1)} = \frac{2iz}{z(1 + i) + 2(1 - i)}.$$

The required extended Möbius transformation is therefore $\widehat{f}$, where

$$f(z) = \frac{2iz}{z(1 + i) + 2(1 - i)}.$$

Alternatively, we could use the results of Problem 2.8, parts (a) and (b), to find the required extended Möbius transformation as

$$\widehat{f} = \widehat{k}^{-1} \circ \widehat{h},$$

where

$$h(z) = \frac{-iz + 2i}{z + 2} \quad \text{and} \quad k(z) = \frac{z - i}{z - 1}.$$

Section 3

3.1 The circle $C = \{z : |z - (1 + i)| = \sqrt{2}\}$ passes through the points 0, 2 and $2i$.

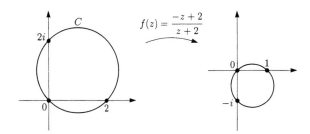

Now

$$\widehat{f}(0) = 1, \quad \widehat{f}(2) = 0 \quad \widehat{f}(2i) = \frac{-2i + 2}{2i + 2} = -i.$$

So the image of C is the generalized circle that passes through the points 1, 0 and $-i$. From the figure, it is evident that this is the circle of radius $1/\sqrt{2}$, centred at $(1 - i)/2$. Thus the image is the circle

$$\left\{z : |z - \tfrac{1}{2}(1 - i)| = 1/\sqrt{2}\right\}.$$

3.2 The line L passes through the points 0, $1 + i$ and ∞.

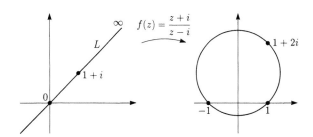

Now

$$\widehat{f}(0) = -1, \quad \widehat{f}(1 + i) = 1 + 2i \quad \text{and} \quad \widehat{f}(\infty) = 1.$$

So the image of L is the generalized circle that passes through the points -1, $1 + 2i$ and 1. Thus the image is the circle

$$\{z : |z - i| = \sqrt{2}\}.$$

3.3 Here $\widehat{f}$ maps 1 to ∞. Since 1 lies on C, the image of C must be an extended line. In fact we have
$$\widehat{f}(1) = \infty, \quad \widehat{f}(i) = (i+1)/(i-1) = -i, \quad \widehat{f}(-1) = 0.$$
So the image of C is the extended line through 0 and $-i$. Thus the image is the extended imaginary axis
$$\{z : \operatorname{Re} z = 0\} \cup \{\infty\}.$$

3.4 By Theorem 2.3,
$$f^{-1}(w) = \frac{w+i}{-w+1}.$$
So w is a point on the image $\widehat{f}(C)$ if and only if $\widehat{f}^{-1}(w)$ lies on the unit circle C, that is, if and only if either $w = \infty$ or
$$\left| \frac{w+i}{-w+1} \right| = 1.$$
An equation for the 'finite' points of the image is therefore
$$|w+i| = |-w+1|.$$
Thus the image of C is the extended line whose 'finite' points are equidistant from the points $-i$ and 1. Thus the image is
$$\{w : |w+i| = |-w+1|\} \cup \{\infty\}.$$

3.5 (a) Since C has equation $|z - (i+1)| = \sqrt{2}$, it follows from the corollary to Theorem 3.1 that $i+1$ and ∞ are inverse points with respect to C. But
$$\widehat{f}(i+1) = i \quad \text{and} \quad \widehat{f}(\infty) = 1.$$
So, by Theorem 3.2, i and 1 are inverse points with respect to $\widehat{f}(C)$.

By Theorem 3.1, $\widehat{f}(C)$ has an equation of the form
$$|w-i| = k|w-1|, \quad \text{for some } k > 0.$$
Since 0 lies on C, it follows that $\widehat{f}(0) = -i$ lies on $\widehat{f}(C)$, and so
$$k = \frac{|-i-i|}{|-i-1|} = \frac{2}{\sqrt{2}} = \sqrt{2}.$$
An Apollonian form of the equation for $\widehat{f}(C)$, which is a circle, is therefore
$$|w-i| = \sqrt{2}|w-1|.$$

(b) Here 1 and ∞ are inverse points with respect to C. So, by Theorem 3.2, $\widehat{f}(1) = 0$ and $\widehat{f}(\infty) = 1$, are inverse points with respect to $\widehat{f}(C)$.

By Theorem 3.1, $\widehat{f}(C)$ has an equation of the form
$$|w| = k|w-1|, \quad \text{for some } k > 0.$$
Since 0 lies on C, it follows that $\widehat{f}(0) = -i$ lies on $\widehat{f}(C)$, and so
$$k = \frac{|-i|}{|-i-1|} = \frac{1}{\sqrt{2}}.$$
An Apollonian form of the equation for $\widehat{f}(C)$, which is a circle, is therefore
$$|w| = |w-1|/\sqrt{2} \quad \text{or} \quad |w-1| = \sqrt{2}|w|.$$

(c) Here i and ∞ are inverse points with respect to C. So, by Theorem 3.2, $\widehat{f}(i) = \infty$ and $\widehat{f}(\infty) = 1$, are inverse points with respect to $\widehat{f}(C)$.

By Theorem 3.1, $\widehat{f}(C)$ has an equation of the form
$$|w-1| = r, \quad \text{for some } r > 0.$$
Since 0 lies on C, it follows that $\widehat{f}(0) = -i$ lies on $\widehat{f}(C)$, and so
$$r = |-i-1| = \sqrt{2}.$$
It follows that $\widehat{f}(C)$ is a circle with equation
$$|w-1| = \sqrt{2}.$$

(d) Here $1+i$ and ∞ are inverse points with respect to C. So, by Theorem 3.2, $\widehat{f}(1+i) = i$ and $\widehat{f}(\infty) = 1$ are inverse points with respect to $\widehat{f}(C)$.

By Theorem 3.1, $\widehat{f}(C)$ has an equation of the form
$$|w-i| = k|w-1|, \quad \text{for some } k > 0.$$
Since 1 lies on C, it follows that $\widehat{f}(1) = 0$ lies on $\widehat{f}(C)$, and so
$$k = \frac{|-i|}{|-1|} = 1.$$
An Apollonian form of the equation for $\widehat{f}(C)$, which is an extended line, is therefore
$$|w-i| = |w-1|.$$

3.6 (a) By Theorem 3.3, the circle with equation
$$|z-i| = \sqrt{2}|z-1|$$
has centre
$$\lambda = \frac{i - 2 \cdot 1}{1 - 2} = 2 - i,$$
and radius
$$r = \frac{\sqrt{2}|i-1|}{|1-2|} = 2.$$

(b) By Theorem 3.3, the circle with equation
$$|z-1| = \sqrt{2}|z|$$
has centre
$$\lambda = \frac{1 - 2 \cdot 0}{1 - 2} = -1,$$
and radius
$$r = \frac{\sqrt{2}|1-0|}{|1-2|} = \sqrt{2}.$$

3.7 Here C has centre 2 and radius 1, so $\lambda = 2$ and $r = 1$. Thus, from Equation (3.3),
$$\alpha - 2 = 1^2 / \left(\overline{(1+i) - 2} \right)$$
$$= 1/(\overline{-1+i}) = \frac{-1+i}{2}.$$
Thus $\alpha = \frac{1}{2}(3+i)$, and so C has an equation of the form
$$\left| z - \tfrac{1}{2}(3+i) \right| = k|z - (1+i)|,$$
where, since 1 lies on C,
$$k = \frac{\left| -\tfrac{1}{2} - \tfrac{1}{2}i \right|}{|-i|} = \sqrt{2}/2,$$
that is, an equation for C is
$$\left| z - \tfrac{1}{2}(3+i) \right| = \tfrac{1}{2}\sqrt{2}|z - (1+i)|.$$

3.8 **(a)** The reflection of the point $2 + 3i$ in L is $-2 + 3i$, and so, by Theorem 3.3(b), $\alpha = -2 + 3i$. An equation for L in Apollonian form is therefore

$$|z - (-2 + 3i)| = |z - (2 + 3i)|.$$

(b) The reflection of the point $4 - 2i$ in L is $2 - 2i$, and so, by Theorem 3.3(b), $\alpha = 2 - 2i$. An equation for L in Apollonian form is therefore

$$|z - (2 - 2i)| = |z - (4 - 2i)|.$$

(c) The reflection of the point $2i$ in L is 2, and so, by Theorem 3.3(b), $\alpha = 2$. An equation for L in Apollonian form is therefore

$$|z - 2i| = |z - 2|.$$

Section 4

4.1 **(a)** $\{z : |z| = 2\}$

(b) $\{z : \operatorname{Re} z = 1\} \cup \{\infty\}$

(c) $\{z : |z| = 3\}$

(d) $\{z : |z| = 3\} \cup \{\infty\}$

4.2 The boundary of D is the unit circle $C = \{z : |z| = 1\}$. In the solution to Problem 3.3 we used the fact that

$$\widehat{f}(1) = \infty, \quad \widehat{f}(i) = -i \quad \text{and} \quad \widehat{f}(-1) = 0$$

to show that the image of this boundary is the extended imaginary axis. Since neither of the singularities of f belongs to D, it follows, from Theorem 4.1, that $f(D)$ is a region whose boundary in $\widehat{\mathbb{C}}$ is the extended imaginary axis.

But there are only two regions that have the extended imaginary axis as a boundary in $\widehat{\mathbb{C}}$, namely the left and right open half-planes.

Since D is on the left of a point which moves on C from 1 to -1 via i, it follows that $f(D)$ lies on the left of the image point as it moves up the imaginary axis. This shows that $f(D)$ is the open left half-plane.

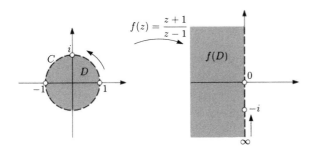

Alternatively, you can use the fact that f maps a point in D to the open left half-plane; for example, $f(0) = -1$.

4.3 The boundary in $\widehat{\mathbb{C}}$ of $\mathcal{R}$ is the set $C \cup \{i\}$, where C is the circle $\{z : |z - i| = 1\}$. In Problem 3.5(c), we showed that the image of C is the circle $\{w : |w - 1| = \sqrt{2}\}$. Also, $\widehat{f}(i) = \infty$, and so by Theorem 4.1, $f(\mathcal{R})$ is a region whose boundary in $\widehat{\mathbb{C}}$ is the set

$$\{w : |w - 1| = \sqrt{2}\} \cup \{\infty\}.$$

But since $\{w : |w - 1| > \sqrt{2}\}$ is the only region that has this set as a boundary it follows that

$$f(\mathcal{R}) = \{w : |w - 1| > \sqrt{2}\} \subseteq \mathbb{C}.$$

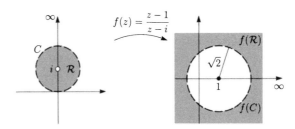

To obtain the image under $\widehat{f}$ of the disc $D = \mathcal{R} \cup \{i\}$, we simply attach the image of i to the image of $\mathcal{R}$ under f, to obtain the generalized disc

$$\widehat{f}(D) = \{w : |w - 1| > \sqrt{2}\} \cup \{\infty\}.$$

4.4 The boundary of D is the circle $C = \{z : |z - 2| = 1\}$ and the boundary in $\widehat{\mathbb{C}}$ of the open upper half-plane is the extended real axis. We shall construct a Möbius transformation that sends a point moving around C from 3 to 1 via $2 + i$, to a point moving along the extended real axis from 0 to ∞ via 1. Since D is on the left of the point as it moves around C, the image of D will be on the left of the image point as it moves along the real axis. This will ensure that the image of D is the open upper half-plane, as required.

So a suitable Möbius transformation sends 3 to 0, $2 + i$ to 1, and 1 to ∞, and this is given by Formula (2.2):

$$f(z) = \frac{(z - 3)}{(z - 1)} \frac{((2 + i) - 1)}{((2 + i) - 3)}$$

$$= \left(\frac{z - 3}{z - 1}\right)\left(\frac{1 + i}{-1 + i}\right) = \frac{-iz + 3i}{z - 1}.$$

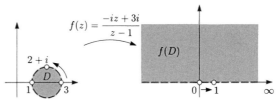

4.5 The boundary in $\widehat{\mathbb{C}}$ of the open half-plane D is the extended line with inverse points 0 and 2. We can construct a suitable Möbius transformation by mapping these inverse points to the inverse points 0 and ∞ with respect to the unit circle. Since $0 \in D$, we can ensure that D maps onto an open disc centered at the origin by mapping 0 to 0 and 2 to ∞. To fix the Möbius transformation completely we map the point ∞ on the boundary of D to the point 1 on the unit circle. The Möbius transformation that does this is

$$f(z) = \frac{z}{z - 2}.$$

4.6 First notice that the function
$f(w) = (-w + 1)/(w + 1)$ is one-one from $\mathbb{C} - \{-1\}$ onto
$\mathbb{C} - \{-1\}$. So, provided that $w \neq -1$ and $z \neq 0, -i$, we
have

$$w = \frac{1}{2i}\left(z - \frac{1}{z}\right) \iff f(w) = f((z - 1/z)/2i)$$
$$\iff \frac{-w + 1}{w + 1} = \frac{-(z - 1/z)/2i + 1}{(z - 1/z)/2i + 1}$$
$$\iff \frac{-w + 1}{w + 1} = \frac{-z^2 + 1 + 2iz}{z^2 - 1 + 2iz}$$
$$\iff \frac{-w + 1}{w + 1} = \left(\frac{iz + 1}{z + i}\right)^2,$$

as required.

4.7 **(a)** The cut plane $\mathcal{R}$ can be regarded as a sector
which has the angle 2π at its vertex. By applying the
principal square root function, we can halve the angle at
the vertex to obtain the open right half-plane $\mathcal{R}_1$. From
here we can reach the open unit disc by applying the
Möbius transformation given by $w = (z_1 - 1)/(z_1 + 1)$,
used in the second example of Frame 1.

On composing this Möbius transformation with the
principal square root function, we obtain the following
mapping from $\mathcal{R}$ onto $\mathcal{S}$:

$$f(z) = \frac{\sqrt{z} - 1}{\sqrt{z} + 1} \quad (z \in \mathcal{R}).$$

This is conformal on $\mathcal{R}$ because the principal square root
function is conformal on $\mathcal{R}$ and the Möbius
transformation is conformal on $\mathcal{R}_1$.

(b) The composite function f is one-one on $\mathcal{R}$ (because
its constituent functions are one-one), and so f has an
inverse function that can be obtained by composing the
inverse of the square root function with the inverse of the
Möbius transformation (see Frame 1). This gives

$$f^{-1}(w) = \left(\frac{w + 1}{-w + 1}\right)^2 \quad (w \in \mathcal{S}).$$

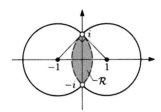

4.8 **(a)** The lens is the region enclosed by two circles
that intersect at right angles at i and $-i$.

We can send the lens to a quadrant that has a vertex at
the origin by sending i to 0 and $-i$ to ∞, using an
extended Möbius transformation which sends circles
through i and $-i$ onto extended lines through 0. An
extended Möbius transformation that will do this is given
by

$$z_1 = \frac{z - i}{z + i}.$$

Under this extended Möbius transformation ∞ is sent
to 1, so the extended imaginary axis is sent to the
extended real axis. Since the circles that form the
boundary of $\mathcal{R}$ make an angle of $\pi/4$ with the imaginary
axis, it follows that the boundary lines of the quadrant
must make an angle of $\pi/4$ with the real axis. The only
quadrant that does this and contains the point -1,
corresponding to $z = 0$, is the one labelled $\mathcal{R}_1$ in the
figure below.

The square function can now be used to open $\mathcal{R}_1$ up onto
the open right half-plane $\mathcal{S}$.

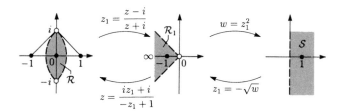

Since the Möbius transformation is one-one and
conformal on $\mathcal{R}$ and the square function is one-one and
conformal on $\mathcal{R}_1$, the composite function

$$f(z) = \left(\frac{z - i}{z + i}\right)^2 \quad (z \in \mathcal{R})$$

is a one-one conformal mapping from $\mathcal{R}$ onto $\mathcal{S}$.

(b) Since f is one-one it has an inverse function that we
can obtain by composing the inverses of the constituent
mappings. The inverse function of the square function is
given by $z_1 = -\sqrt{w}$, and the inverse function of the
Möbius transformation is given by
$z = (iz_1 + i)/(-z_1 + 1)$, so

$$f^{-1}(w) = \frac{-i\sqrt{w} + i}{\sqrt{w} + 1} \quad (w \in \mathcal{S}).$$

4.9 **(a)** We have

$$\tan(\pi/2 - z) = \frac{\sin(\pi/2 - z)}{\cos(\pi/2 - z)} \quad \text{(by definition)}$$
$$= \frac{\sin(\pi/2)\cos(-z) + \cos(\pi/2)\sin(-z)}{\cos(\pi/2)\cos(-z) - \sin(\pi/2)\sin(-z)}$$
$$= \frac{1 \cdot \cos z - 0 \cdot \sin z}{0 \cdot \cos z + 1 \cdot \sin z}$$
$$\quad \text{(Unit A2, Theorem 4.3)}$$
$$= \frac{\cos z}{\sin z} = \cot z \quad \text{(by definition)}.$$

Alternatively, we could appeal to the geometrically
obvious fact that, if z is real and $z \in\ ]0, \pi/2[$, then

$$\cot z = \tan(\pi/2 - z),$$

and then apply the Uniqueness Theorem (*Unit B3*,
Theorem 5.5).

(b) Since the linear function

$$z_1 = \pi/2 - z$$

maps the open strip $\mathcal{R} = \{z : 0 < \operatorname{Re} z < \pi\}$ onto the
open strip $\mathcal{R}_1 = \{z : -\pi/2 < \operatorname{Re} z_1 < \pi/2\}$, it follows from
Frame 4 that the function

$$\cot z = \tan(\pi/2 - z)$$

maps $\mathcal{R}$ onto $\mathcal{S} = \mathbb{C} - \{iv : |v| \geq 1\}$.

(c) If $z_1 = \pi/2 - z$, then
$$w = \tan z_1 = \cot z;$$
hence if we take $\cot^{-1} w = z$, then
$$\begin{aligned} \cot^{-1} w &= \pi/2 - z_1 \\ &= \pi/2 - \tan^{-1} w \\ &= \frac{\pi}{2} - \frac{1}{2i} \operatorname{Log}\left(\frac{1+iw}{1-iw}\right) \quad (w \in \mathcal{S}). \end{aligned}$$

4.10 (a) From Frame 5, we have
$$\sin^{-1} w = \frac{1}{i} \operatorname{Log}\left(\frac{i\sqrt{\dfrac{1-w}{1+w}} - 1}{-\sqrt{\dfrac{1-w}{1+w}} + i}\right),$$
where, for convenience, we have written $\dfrac{-w+1}{w+1}$ as $\dfrac{1-w}{1+w}$.

So, if $w \in \{x \in \mathbb{R} : |x| < 1\}$, then the expression in brackets is
$$\begin{aligned} &\frac{i\sqrt{1-w} - \sqrt{1+w}}{-\sqrt{1-w} + i\sqrt{1+w}} \\ &= \left(\frac{i\sqrt{1-w} - \sqrt{1+w}}{-\sqrt{1-w} + i\sqrt{1+w}}\right)\left(\frac{-\sqrt{1-w} - i\sqrt{1+w}}{-\sqrt{1-w} - i\sqrt{1+w}}\right) \\ &= \frac{-i(1-w) + 2\sqrt{1-w}\sqrt{1+w} + i(1+w)}{(1-w) + (1+w)} \\ &= iw + \sqrt{1-w^2}. \end{aligned}$$

Thus, for these values of w,
$$\sin^{-1} w = \frac{1}{i} \operatorname{Log}\left(iw + \sqrt{1-w^2}\right).$$

(b) If $w \in \mathcal{S}$, then $1 - w^2$ belongs to the standard cut plane; see the following figure.

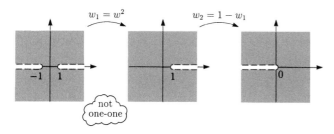

Also if $w \in \mathcal{S}$, then $iw + \sqrt{1-w^2}$ must belong to the standard cut plane. For, if
$$iw + \sqrt{1-w^2} = -a, \quad \text{where } a \geq 0,$$

then
$$\sqrt{1-w^2} = -iw - a \tag{1}$$
$$\Longrightarrow$$
$$1 - w^2 = (-iw - a)^2$$
$$\Longrightarrow$$
$$1 - w^2 = a^2 + 2iaw - w^2$$
$$\Longrightarrow$$
$$1 = a^2 + 2iaw \quad (\text{so that } a \neq 0)$$
$$\Longrightarrow$$
$$iw = \frac{1 - a^2}{2a}.$$

By substituting this value of iw into Equation (1), we deduce that
$$\sqrt{1-w^2} = -\frac{1-a^2}{2a} - a = -\frac{1+a^2}{2a} < 0.$$
But this cannot be true since a principal square root cannot be a negative real number.

(c) From part (b) we know that the function $f(w) = (1/i)\operatorname{Log}\left(iw + \sqrt{1-w^2}\right)$ is defined, and analytic, throughout $\mathcal{S}$. Also, by part (a), we know that $(1/i)\operatorname{Log}\left(iw + \sqrt{1-w^2}\right)$ agrees with $\sin^{-1} w$ on $\{x \in \mathbb{R} : |x| < 1\}$. Thus it follows from the Uniqueness Theorem that
$$\sin^{-1} w = \frac{1}{i} \operatorname{Log}\left(iw + \sqrt{1-w^2}\right), \quad \text{for } w \in \mathcal{S}.$$

(d) The derivative of sin is cos, which is non-zero throughout $\mathcal{R} = \{z : -\pi/2 < \operatorname{Re} z < \pi/2\}$. By the Inverse Function Rule, it follows that $\sin^{-1}$ is analytic on $\mathcal{S}$ and that
$$\left(\sin^{-1}\right)'(w) = \frac{1}{\cos\left(\sin^{-1}(w)\right)}, \quad \text{for } w \in \mathcal{S}.$$

Now if $w \in \{x \in \mathbb{R} : |x| < 1\}$, then $\sin^{-1} w$ is a real number between $-\pi/2$ and $\pi/2$, and so $\cos\left(\sin^{-1} w\right)$ is a positive real number. We can therefore write, for such w,
$$\begin{aligned} \left(\sin^{-1}\right)'(w) &= \frac{1}{\cos\left(\sin^{-1}(w)\right)} \\ &= \frac{1}{\sqrt{1 - \sin^2\left(\sin^{-1} w\right)}} \\ &= \frac{1}{\sqrt{1 - w^2}}. \end{aligned}$$

But we already know that the expression $\sqrt{1-w^2}$, and hence $1/\sqrt{1-w^2}$, defines an analytic function throughout $\mathcal{S}$, and so, by the Uniqueness Theorem,
$$\left(\sin^{-1}\right)'(w) = \frac{1}{\sqrt{1-w^2}}, \quad \text{for } w \in \mathcal{S}.$$

SOLUTIONS TO THE EXERCISES

Section 1

1.1 **(a)** Rotating the half-plane $\{z : \operatorname{Im} z > 1\}$ about 0 through $\pi/2$ clockwise and translating the result one unit to the right gives the half-plane $\{z : \operatorname{Re} z > 2\}$. The linear function which does this is
$$f(z) = e^{-i\pi/2}z + 1 = -iz + 1.$$

(b) Translating the disc $\{z : |z - i| < 1\}$ one unit in the negative y direction and then scaling the result by the factor 10 gives the disc $\{z : |z| < 10\}$. The linear function which does this is
$$f(z) = 10(z - i).$$

1.2 **(a)** Using the result of Problem 1.5(b) or the comment following that problem, we obtain the following types of image under the reciprocal function.

(i) The image of the line $2x - y = 0$ is a line through the origin.

(ii) The image of the circle $x^2 + y^2 = 2$ is a circle not through the origin.

(iii) The image of the circle $x^2 + (y - 2)^2 = 4$ is a line not through the origin.

(iv) The image of the line $2x + y = 1$ is a circle through the origin.

(Note that the origin is not in the domain or image of the reciprocal function, and so 'lines and circles through the origin' must be interpreted appropriately.)

(b) (i) In $2x - y = 0$, we replace x by $u/(u^2 + v^2)$ and y by $-v/(u^2 + v^2)$ to obtain
$$\frac{2u}{u^2 + v^2} + \frac{v}{u^2 + v^2} = 0,$$
that is, $2u + v = 0$.

(ii) In $x^2 + y^2 = 2$, we replace x by $u/(u^2 + v^2)$ and y by $-v(u^2 + v^2)$ to obtain
$$\frac{u^2}{(u^2 + v^2)^2} + \frac{v^2}{(u^2 + v^2)^2} = 2.$$
By multiplying throughout by $u^2 + v^2$, we obtain
$$1 = 2\left(u^2 + v^2\right),$$
that is, $u^2 + v^2 = \frac{1}{2}$.

1.3 **(a)** For $f(z) = 2z + 6$, we have
$$f(1/w) = (2/w) + 6 \to \infty \text{ as } w \to 0,$$
so f has a pole at ∞. Thus
$$\widehat{f}(z) = \begin{cases} f(z), & z \in \mathbb{C}, \\ \infty, & z = \infty. \end{cases}$$

(b) For $f(z) = 1/(z - 1)$, we have
$$f(z) \to \infty \text{ as } z \to 1,$$
so $\widehat{f}(1) = \infty$. Also
$$\lim_{w \to 0} f(1/w) = \lim_{w \to 0} \frac{1}{1/w - 1}$$
$$= \lim_{w \to 0} \frac{w}{1 - w} = 0,$$
so f has a removable singularity at ∞, with $\widehat{f}(\infty) = 0$.

Thus
$$\widehat{f}(z) = \begin{cases} f(z), & z \in \mathbb{C} - \{1\}, \\ \infty, & z = 1, \\ 0, & z = \infty. \end{cases}$$

Section 2

2.1 **(a)** f is not Möbius: $ad - bc = 1 \cdot 1 - (-i) \cdot (i) = 0$.
g is Möbius: $a = 1$, $b = -1$, $c = 1$, $d = 2i$;
$ad - bc = 2i + 1 \neq 0$.
h is Möbius: $a = 1$, $b = 0$, $c = 2$, $d = -i$;
$ad - bc = -i \neq 0$.

(b) The extended Möbius transformations are:
$$\widehat{g}(z) = \begin{cases} g(z), & z \in \mathbb{C} - \{-2i\}, \\ \infty, & z = -2i, \\ 1, & z = \infty; \end{cases}$$
and
$$\widehat{h}(z) = \begin{cases} h(z), & z \in \mathbb{C} - \left\{\frac{1}{2}i\right\}, \\ \infty, & z = \frac{1}{2}i, \\ \frac{1}{2}, & z = \infty. \end{cases}$$
By Theorem 2.3, the inverse functions of g and h are
$$g^{-1}(z) = \frac{2iz + 1}{-z + 1} \quad \text{and} \quad h^{-1}(z) = \frac{-iz}{-2z + 1},$$
respectively.

2.2 For z in the domain of $g \circ f$, we have
$$(\widehat{g} \circ \widehat{f})(z) = g\left(\frac{z + 1}{z - 1}\right) = \frac{\dfrac{z + 1}{z - 1} - 2}{\dfrac{z + 1}{z - 1} + i}$$
$$= \frac{(z + 1) - 2(z - 1)}{(z + 1) + i(z - 1)}$$
$$= \frac{-z + 3}{(1 + i)z + (1 - i)}.$$

So, by Theorem 2.4, $\widehat{g} \circ \widehat{f}$ is the extended Möbius transformation corresponding to h, where
$$h(z) = \frac{-z + 3}{(1 + i)z + (1 - i)}.$$

2.3 In each case we use Formula (2.2). The extended Möbius transformation is $\widehat{f}$, where

(a) $f(z) = \dfrac{(z - 1)}{(z - \infty)} \dfrac{(-1 - \infty)}{(-1 - 1)} = \dfrac{z - 1}{-2} = -\frac{1}{2}z + \frac{1}{2}$;

(b) $f(z) = \dfrac{(z - 1)}{(z - (-1))} \dfrac{(0 - (-1))}{(0 - 1)} = \dfrac{z - 1}{-z - 1} = \dfrac{-z + 1}{z + 1}$;

(c) $f(z) = \dfrac{(z - (1 + i))}{(z - 0)} \dfrac{((2 - i) - 0)}{((2 - i) - (1 + i))}$
$$= \frac{(2 - i)z - (3 + i)}{(1 - 2i)z}.$$

2.4 We find the required transformation by using the Implicit Formula, which in this case is
$$\frac{(z - 2i)}{(z - 1)} \frac{((1 + 2i) - 1)}{((1 + 2i) - 2i)} = \frac{(w - 1)}{(w - i)} \frac{((1 + i) - i)}{((1 + i) - 1)}.$$
By evaluating the constant terms and cross-multiplying, we obtain
$$(z - 2i)(w - i)(2i) = (w - 1)(z - 1)(-i),$$

that is,
$$2zwi + 4w + 2z - 4i = -wzi + iw + iz - i.$$
On collecting the w terms on the left, we obtain
$$3wzi + (4 - i)w = (-2 + i)z + 3i,$$
and so
$$w = \frac{(-2 + i)z + 3i}{3iz + (4 - i)}.$$
The required extended Möbius transformation is $\widehat{f}$, where
$$f(z) = \frac{(-2 + i)z + 3i}{3iz + (4 - i)}.$$

Section 3

3.1 **(a)** Here $\widehat{f}$ maps 2 to ∞. Since 2 lies on C, the image of C is an extended line. Also
$$\widehat{f}(-2i) = 0 \quad \text{and} \quad \widehat{f}(-2) = \tfrac{1}{2} - \tfrac{1}{2}i.$$
Thus the image $\widehat{f}(C)$ is the extended line
$$\{z : \operatorname{Re} z = -\operatorname{Im} z\} \cup \{\infty\}.$$

(b) If we choose the three (convenient) points $2, -2, 2i$ on C, then
$$\widehat{f}(2) = 0, \quad \widehat{f}(-2) = 2, \quad \widehat{f}(2i) = 1 + i.$$
So the image $f(C)$ is the generalized circle which passes through the three points 0, 2 and $1 + i$. (These points are the vertices of an isosceles triangle.)

From the figure, it is evident that this circle has centre at $\alpha = 1$ and radius 1. Hence
$$\widehat{f}(C) = \{z : |z - 1| = 1\}.$$

3.2 **(a)** The centre of $C = \{z : |z + i| = 1\}$ is $-i$, and so it follows, from the corollary to Theorem 3.1, that $-i$ and ∞ are inverse points with respect to C.
Hence, by Theorem 3.2,
$$\widehat{f}(-i) = \infty \quad \text{and} \quad \widehat{f}(\infty) = 1$$
are inverse points with respect to $\widehat{f}(C)$, and so, by Theorem 3.1, $\widehat{f}(C)$ has an equation of the form
$$|w - 1| = r, \quad \text{for some } r > 0.$$
Since 0 lies on C, $\widehat{f}(0) = -1$ lies on $\widehat{f}(C)$, and so
$$r = |-1 - 1| = 2.$$
It follows that $\widehat{f}(C)$ is the circle $|w - 1| = 2$.

(b) The centre of $C = \{z : |z - i| = 1\}$ is i, and so it follows, from the corollary to Theorem 3.1, that i and ∞ are inverse points with respect to C.
Hence, by Theorem 3.2,
$$\widehat{f}(i) = 0 \quad \text{and} \quad \widehat{f}(\infty) = 1$$
are inverse points with respect to $\widehat{f}(C)$, and so, by Theorem 3.1, $\widehat{f}(C)$ has an equation of the form
$$|w| = k|w - 1|, \quad \text{for some } k > 0.$$
Since 0 lies on C, $\widehat{f}(0) = -1$ lies on $\widehat{f}(C)$, and so
$$k = \frac{|-1|}{|-1 + i|} = \frac{1}{\sqrt{2}}.$$
It follows that $\widehat{f}(C)$ is the circle $|w - 1| = \sqrt{2}|w|$.

3.3 **(a)** By Theorem 3.3, the circle with equation
$$|z - i| = 2|z + 3i|$$
has centre
$$\lambda = \frac{i - 4(-3i)}{1 - 4} = -\tfrac{13}{3}i$$
and radius
$$r = \frac{2|i - (-3i)|}{|1 - 4|} = \tfrac{8}{3}.$$
(b) By Theorem 3.3, the circle with equation
$$|z| = 6|z + i|$$
has centre
$$\lambda = \frac{0 - 36(-i)}{1 - 36} = -\tfrac{36}{35}i$$
and radius
$$r = \frac{6|0 - (-i)|}{|1 - 36|} = \tfrac{6}{35}.$$

3.4 **(a)** **(i)** The circle C_1 has centre $\lambda = 0$ and radius $r = 2$. Thus, from Equation (3.3) with $\beta = 1 + i$,
$$\alpha - 0 = 2^2/(\overline{(1 + i) - 0}) = 4/(1 - i),$$
so that $\alpha = 2(1 + i)$.
(ii) The circle C_2 has centre $\lambda = i$ and radius $r = \tfrac{1}{2}$. Thus, from Equation (3.3) with $\beta = 1 + i$,
$$\alpha - i = \left(\tfrac{1}{2}\right)^2/(\overline{(1 + i) - i}) = \tfrac{1}{4},$$
so that $\alpha = \tfrac{1}{4} + i$.

(b) **(i)** An Apollonian form of the equation for the circle C_1 is
$$|z - 2(1 + i)| = k|z - (1 + i)|, \quad \text{for some } k > 0.$$
Since 2 lies on C_1,
$$k = \frac{|2 - 2(1 + i)|}{|2 - (1 + i)|} = \sqrt{2},$$
and so C_1 has equation
$$|z - 2(1 + i)| = \sqrt{2}|z - (1 + i)|.$$
(ii) An Apollonian form of the equation for the circle C_2 is
$$\left|z - \left(\tfrac{1}{4} + i\right)\right| = k|z - (1 + i)|, \quad \text{for some } k > 0.$$
Since $\tfrac{1}{2}i$ lies on C_2,
$$k = \frac{\left|\tfrac{1}{2}i - \left(\tfrac{1}{4} + i\right)\right|}{\left|\tfrac{1}{2}i - (1 + i)\right|} = \frac{\left|-\tfrac{1}{4} - \tfrac{1}{2}i\right|}{\left|-1 - \tfrac{1}{2}i\right|} = \tfrac{1}{2},$$
and so C_2 has equation
$$\left|z - \left(\tfrac{1}{4} + i\right)\right| = \tfrac{1}{2}|z - (1 + i)|.$$

3.5 **(a)** The reflection of the point $\beta = 2 - i$ in the extended real axis is $2 + i$, and so, by Theorem 3.3(b), $\alpha = 2 + i$. An equation in Apollonian form for the extended real axis is therefore

$$|z - (2 + i)| = |z - (2 - i)|.$$

(b) The reflection of the point $\beta = 2 - i$ in the extended line $\{z : \operatorname{Re} z + \operatorname{Im} z = 0\} \cup \{\infty\}$ is $1 - 2i$, and so, by Theorem 3.3(b), $\alpha = 1 - 2i$. An equation in Apollonian form for this extended line is therefore

$$|z - (1 - 2i)| = |z - (2 - i)|.$$

Section 4

4.1 **(a)** $\{z : |z - i| = 2\}$

(b) $\{z : \operatorname{Im} z = -1\} \cup \{\infty\}$

(c) $\{z : |z + i| = 1\}$

(d) $\{z : |z + i| = 1\} \cup \{\infty\}$

4.2 **(a)** The boundary in $\widehat{\mathbb{C}}$ of the disc $D = \{z : |z - 1| < 2\}$ is the circle $C = \{z : |z - 1| = 2\}$. The points 3, $1 + 2i$ and -1 on C are such that

$$\widehat{f}(3) = \frac{3 + i}{4} = \tfrac{1}{4}(3 + i), \quad \widehat{f}(1 + 2i) = \frac{1 + 3i}{2 + 2i} = 1 + \tfrac{1}{2}i,$$

and

$$\widehat{f}(-1) = \infty,$$

where $\widehat{f}$ is the extended Möbius transformation associated with f. Thus the image of C under $\widehat{f}$ is the extended line

$$\widehat{f}(C) = \left\{z : \operatorname{Re} z - \operatorname{Im} z = \tfrac{1}{2}\right\} \cup \{\infty\}.$$

Since the disc D is in the domain of f, it follows from Theorem 4.1 that $f(D)$ is a region bounded by the extended line $\widehat{f}(C)$.

Since D is on the left of a point which moves around C from 3 to -1 via $1 + 2i$, it follows that $f(D)$ lies on the left of the extended line $\widehat{f}(C)$ as the image point moves along $\widehat{f}(C)$, from $\tfrac{1}{4}(3 + i)$ to ∞ via $1 + \tfrac{1}{2}i$. This shows that $f(D)$ is the open half-plane

$$f(D) = \left\{z : \operatorname{Re} z - \operatorname{Im} z < \tfrac{1}{2}\right\}.$$

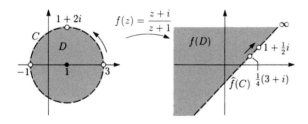

(b) The boundary in $\widehat{\mathbb{C}}$ of the punctured open disc $\mathcal{R} = \{z : 0 < |z + i| < 1\}$ is the set $C \cup \{-i\}$, where C is the circle $\{z : |z + i| = 1\}$. In Exercise 3.2(a), we found that the image of C under $\widehat{f}$ is $\{w : |w - 1| = 2\}$. Also, $\widehat{f}(-i) = \infty$, and so, by Theorem 4.1, $f(\mathcal{R})$ is a region whose boundary in $\widehat{\mathbb{C}}$ is the set

$$\{w : |w - 1| = 2\} \cup \{\infty\}.$$

But since $\{w : |w - 1| > 2\}$ is the only region which has this set as its boundary in $\widehat{\mathbb{C}}$, it follows that

$$f(\mathcal{R}) = \{w : |w - 1| > 2\}.$$

The image under $\widehat{f}$ of the open disc

$$D = \{z : |z + i| < 1\} = \mathcal{R} \cup \{-i\}$$

is

$$\begin{aligned}\widehat{f}(D) &= f(\mathcal{R}) \cup \widehat{f}(-i) \\ &= \{w : |w - 1| > 2\} \cup \{\infty\}.\end{aligned}$$

4.3 The boundary in $\widehat{\mathbb{C}}$ of the open half-plane

$$H = \{z : \operatorname{Im} z + \operatorname{Re} z < 1\}$$

is the extended line with inverse points 0 and $1 + i$. Since $0 \in H$, we can ensure that H maps onto an open disc centred at 0 by mapping 0 to 0, and $1 + i$ to ∞. To ensure that H maps onto the disc with radius 2 (and centre 0), we map ∞ (which is on the boundary in $\widehat{\mathbb{C}}$ of H) to 2. The required extended Möbius transformation which does this is $\widehat{f}$, where

$$f(z) = \frac{2z}{z - (1 + i)}.$$

4.4 Let $f(z) = 1/z$ and consider the images under the extended reciprocal function $\widehat{f}$ of the points

$$2, 1 + i, 0 \text{ on } C_1 = \{z : |z - 1| = 1\}$$

and

$$4, 2 + 2i, 0 \text{ on } C_2 = \{z : |z - 2| = 2\}.$$

We have

$$\widehat{f}(2) = \tfrac{1}{2}, \quad \widehat{f}(1 + i) = \tfrac{1}{2} - \tfrac{1}{2}i, \quad \widehat{f}(0) = \infty$$

and

$$\widehat{f}(4) = \tfrac{1}{4}, \quad \widehat{f}(2 + 2i) = \tfrac{1}{4} - \tfrac{1}{4}i.$$

Thus the image under $\widehat{f}$ of C_1 is $\left\{z_1 : \operatorname{Re} z_1 = \tfrac{1}{2}\right\}$ and of C_2 is $\left\{z_1 : \operatorname{Re} z_1 = \tfrac{1}{4}\right\}$, where $z_1 = f(z) = 1/z$.

Since $3 \in \mathcal{R}$ and $\widehat{f}(3) = \tfrac{1}{3}$, it follows that

$$\widehat{f}(\mathcal{R}) = \left\{z_1 : \tfrac{1}{4} < \operatorname{Re} z_1 < \tfrac{1}{2}\right\} = \mathcal{R}_1, \text{ say.}$$

(Note that the image intersects the real axis at right angles, as expected.)

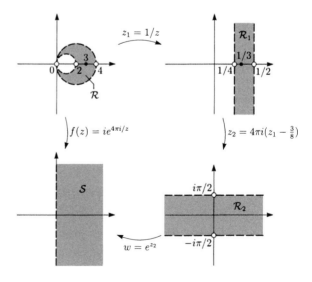

Now, we can map $\mathcal{R}_1$ onto $\mathcal{R}_2 = \{z_2 : -\pi/2 < \operatorname{Im} z_2 < \pi/2\}$ using the linear function given by

$$z_2 = 4\pi i \left(z_1 - \tfrac{3}{8}\right),$$

which sends $\tfrac{3}{8}$ to 0, expands the width of the strip by a factor of 4π, and rotates it anticlockwise about 0 by $\pi/2$.

We can now use the exponential function given by $w = e^{z_2}$ to map the strip $\mathcal{R}_2$ onto the open right half-plane $\mathcal{S}$ (see Frame 1). Thus the required function is

$$f(z) = e^{z_2} = e^{4\pi i(z_1 - 3/8)}$$
$$= e^{4\pi i(1/z - 3/8)}$$
$$= e^{4\pi i/z} e^{-3\pi i/2}$$
$$= i e^{4\pi i/z}.$$

This function is a one-one conformal mapping, since the constituent functions are one-one and conformal.

4.5 **(a)** Let f be a Möbius transformation which maps the open unit disc D onto itself, and let $\alpha \in D$ and $\beta \in \widehat{\mathbb{C}}$ be such that

$$\alpha = \widehat{f}^{-1}(0) \quad \text{and} \quad \beta = \widehat{f}^{-1}(\infty),$$

where $\widehat{f}^{-1}$ is the inverse function of the extended Möbius transformation associated with f. Then α and β are inverse points with respect to the unit circle $\{z : |z| = 1\}$, and so, from Equation (3.3),

$$\beta = 1/\overline{\alpha}. \tag{1}$$

Hence, from Formula (2.2), f is of the form

$$f(z) = \lambda \left(\frac{z - \alpha}{z - \beta} \right), \quad \text{for some } \lambda \in \mathbb{C},$$
$$= \overline{\alpha}\lambda \left(\frac{z - \alpha}{\overline{\alpha}z - 1} \right) \quad \text{(by Equation (1)).} \tag{2}$$

It follows from Theorem 4.1 that $\widehat{f}$ maps the unit circle onto the unit circle, and so $|f(1)| = 1$. Hence, from Equation (2),

$$1 = |f(1)| = |\overline{\alpha}\lambda| \left| \frac{1 - \alpha}{\overline{\alpha} - 1} \right|$$
$$= |\overline{\alpha}\lambda|,$$

since $|1 - \alpha| = |1 - \overline{\alpha}| = |\overline{\alpha} - 1|$.
Thus $|\overline{\alpha}\lambda| = 1$, and so

$$\overline{\alpha}\lambda = e^{i\theta}, \quad \text{where } \theta \in \mathbb{R};$$

hence

$$f(z) = e^{i\theta} \left(\frac{z - \alpha}{\overline{\alpha}z - 1} \right),$$

where $|\alpha| < 1$ and $\theta \in \mathbb{R}$.

(b) Since $f(0) = 0$, we have $\alpha = 0$, and so f is of the form

$$f(z) = -e^{i\theta} z.$$

Hence

$$f'(z) = -e^{i\theta}.$$

Since $f'(0) > 0$, it follows that $-e^{i\theta} = 1$, and so f has the form

$$f(z) = z.$$

Hence the only Möbius transformation f which maps the open unit disc onto itself and satisfies $f(0) = 0$ and $f'(0) > 0$ is the identity function

$$f(z) = z.$$